Published by CGP

Editors:
Katie Braid, Charlotte Burrows, Katherine Faudemer, Robin Flello, Emily Forsberg, Emily Howe, Sharon Keeley-Holden,
Duncan Lindsay, Chris McGarry, Sarah Pattison, Frances Rooney, Charlotte Whiteley, Sarah Williams and Jonathan Wray.

Contributors:
Sophie Anderson, Ian Davis, Alison Dennis, John Duffy, Mark A. Edwards, Mark Ellingham, James Foster, Barbara Mascetti,
Bethan Parry, Alison Popperwell and Chris Workman.

ISBN 978 1 78294 485 0

With thanks to Rachael Marshall, Sophie Scott, Hayley Thompson and Karen Wells for the proofreading.
With thanks to Jan Greenway and Ana Pungartnik for the copyright research.

Data on the graph on page 165 showing the change in atmospheric CO_2 concentration provided by Carbon Cycle and Greenhouse Gases group,
325 Broadway R/CSD, Boulder, CO 80305 (http://esrl.noaa.gov/gmd/ccgg/)

Data on the graph on page 165 showing the change in global temperature from GISTEMP Team, 2015: GISS Surface Temperature Analysis
(GISTEMP). NASA Goddard Institute for Space Studies. Dataset accessed 2016-04-11 at http://data.giss.nasa.gov/gistemp/.

Data for the level of carbon dioxide in the atmosphere in the table on page 165: Hansen, J., R. Ruedy, M. Sato, and K. Lo, 2010:
Global surface temperature change, Rev. Geophys., 48, RG4004, doi:10.1029/2010RG000345.

Data for the level of methane in the atmosphere in the table on page 165: IPCC, 2013: Climate Change 2013: The Physical Science Basis.
Contribution of Working Group I to the Fifth Assessment Report of the Intergovernmental Panel on Climate Change
[Stocker, T. F., D. Qin, G.-K. Plattner, M. Tignor, S. K. Allen, J. Boschung, A. Nauels, Y. Xia, V. Bex and P. M. Midgley (eds.)].
Cambridge University Press, Cambridge, United Kingdom and New York, NY, USA. (From Chapter 8.3.2)

Data for the level of CFC-12 in the atmosphere in the table on page 165. IPCC, 2013: Climate Change 2013: The Physical Science Basis.
Contribution of Working Group I to the Fifth Assessment Report of the Intergovernmental Panel on Climate Change
[Stocker, T. F., D. Qin, G.-K. Plattner, M. Tignor, S. K. Allen, J. Boschung, A. Nauels, Y. Xia, V. Bex and P. M. Midgley (eds.)].
Cambridge University Press, Cambridge, United Kingdom and New York, NY, USA. (From Table 8.A.1)

Data for the greenhouse gas lifetimes in the atmosphere and global warming potentials in the table on page 165: SIPCC, 2013: Climate Change
2013: The Physical Science Basis. Contribution of Working Group I to the Fifth Assessment Report of the Intergovernmental Panel on Climate
Change [Stocker, T. F., D. Qin, G.-K. Plattner, M. Tignor, S. K. Allen, J. Boschung, A. Nauels, Y. Xia, V. Bex and P. M. Midgley (eds.)].
Cambridge University Press, Cambridge, United Kingdom and New York, NY, USA. (From Chapter 8, Table 8.A.1)

Table on page 241 contains public sector information licensed under the Open Government Licence v3.0.
http://www.nationalarchives.gov.uk/doc/open-government-licence/version/3/

Every effort has been made to locate copyright holders and obtain permission to reproduce sources. For those sources where it has been difficult
to trace the originator of the work, we would be grateful for information. If any copyright holder would like us to make an amendment to the
acknowledgements, please notify us and we will gladly update the book at the next reprint. Thank you.

Clipart from Corel®
Printed by Elanders Ltd, Newcastle upon Tyne

Based on the classic CGP style created by Richard Parsons.

How to Use This Book

- Hold the book <u>upright</u>, approximately <u>50 cm</u> from your face, ensuring that the text looks like <u>this</u>, not this. Alternatively, place the book on a <u>horizontal</u> surface (e.g. a table or desk) and sit adjacent to the book, at a distance which doesn't make the text too small to read.

- In case of emergency, press the two halves of the book together <u>firmly</u> in order to close.

- Before attempting to use this book, familiarise yourself with the following <u>safety information</u>:

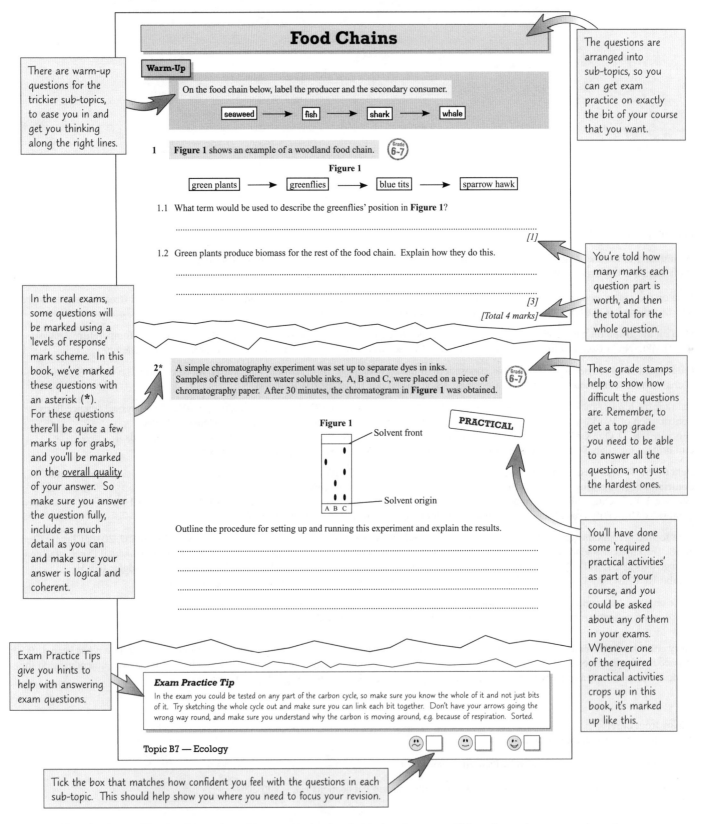

There are warm-up questions for the trickier sub-topics, to ease you in and get you thinking along the right lines.

In the real exams, some questions will be marked using a 'levels of response' mark scheme. In this book, we've marked these questions with an asterisk (*). For these questions there'll be quite a few marks up for grabs, and you'll be marked on the <u>overall quality</u> of your answer. So make sure you answer the question fully, include as much detail as you can and make sure your answer is logical and coherent.

Exam Practice Tips give you hints to help with answering exam questions.

The questions are arranged into sub-topics, so you can get exam practice on exactly the bit of your course that you want.

You're told how many marks each question part is worth, and then the total for the whole question.

These grade stamps help to show how difficult the questions are. Remember, to get a top grade you need to be able to answer all the questions, not just the hardest ones.

You'll have done some 'required practical activities' as part of your course, and you could be asked about any of them in your exams. Whenever one of the required practical activities crops up in this book, it's marked up like this.

Tick the box that matches how confident you feel with the questions in each sub-topic. This should help show you where you need to focus your revision.

Food Chains

Warm-Up

On the food chain below, label the producer and the secondary consumer.

seaweed → fish → shark → whale

1 **Figure 1** shows an example of a woodland food chain.

Figure 1

green plants → greenflies → blue tits → sparrow hawk

1.1 What term would be used to describe the greenflies' position in **Figure 1**?

.... *[1]*

1.2 Green plants produce biomass for the rest of the food chain. Explain how they do this.

....
.... *[3]*

[Total 4 marks]

2* A simple chromatography experiment was set up to separate dyes in inks. Samples of three different water soluble inks, A, B and C, were placed on a piece of chromatography paper. After 30 minutes, the chromatogram in **Figure 1** was obtained.

Figure 1

PRACTICAL

Solvent front

Solvent origin

A B C

Outline the procedure for setting up and running this experiment and explain the results.

....
....
....
....

Exam Practice Tip

In the exam you could be tested on any part of the carbon cycle, so make sure you know the whole of it and not just bits of it. Try sketching the whole cycle out and make sure you can link each bit together. Don't have your arrows going the wrong way round, and make sure you understand why the carbon is moving around, e.g. because of respiration. Sorted.

Topic B7 — Ecology

- There's also a Physics Equations List at the back of this book — you'll be given these equations in your exam. You can look up equations on this list to help you answer some of the physics questions in this book.

Cells

Use the words on the right to correctly fill in the gaps in the passage.
You don't have to use every word, but each word can only be used once.

many
smaller
plant
bacterial
single   larger
animal
simpler

Most eukaryotic organisms are made up of .... cells.

They include .... and .... cells.

Prokaryotic organisms are .... cells. They are

.... and .... than eukaryotic cells.

1   **Figure 1** shows a diagram of an animal cell.

Figure 1

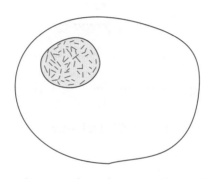

1.1 Label the cell membrane, cytoplasm and nucleus on **Figure 1**.

[3]

1.2 Give the function of each part of the cell on **Figure 1**.

Cell membrane ....

Cytoplasm ....

Nucleus ....

[3]

1.3 Name **two** other subcellular structures that can be found in an animal cell.
Describe the function of each structure.

....

....

....

....

[4]

1.4 Give **one** reason why the diagram in **Figure 1** does not represent a plant cell.

....

[1]

[Total 11 marks]

2 **Figure 2** shows a diagram of a prokaryotic cell.

Figure 2

1 μm

2.1 Which of the following is a prokaryotic cell?
Tick **one** box.

☐ root hair cell   ☐ bacterium   ☐ sperm   ☐ nerve cell

[1]

2.2 Name structures X, Y and Z on **Figure 2**.

X ....

Y ....

Z ....

[3]

2.3 Which of the following is true for structure Z? Tick **one** box.

☐ It is where photosynthesis occurs.

☐ It is part of the cell membrane.

☐ It contains genetic material.

[1]

Look at the scale on **Figure 2**.

2.4 A eukaryotic cell measures 10 μm long.
How many times larger is it than the cell in **Figure 2**?

....

[1]

2.5 The head of a pin is approximately 1 mm in diameter.
How many prokaryotic cells would fit lengthways across it?

.... cells

[2]

2.6 Give **one** difference between prokaryotic and eukaryotic cells, other than their size.

....

....

[1]

[Total 9 marks]

Topic B1 — Cell Biology   ☹ ☐   ☺ ☐   ☺ ☐

Microscopy

1 A student observed blood cells under a microscope.
A scale drawing of one of the cells is shown in **Figure 1**.

Figure 1

A

In **Figure 1**, A is the image width. The real width of the cell is 0.012 mm.
What is the magnification of the image? Use the formula:

$$\text{magnification} = \frac{\text{size of image}}{\text{size of real object}}$$

magnification = × ....

[Total 2 marks]

2 A plant cell is magnified 1000 times using a light microscope.

2.1 The length of the image of the plant cell is 10 mm.
Calculate the actual length of one plant cell in millimetres (mm).
Use the formula:

$$\text{magnification} = \frac{\text{size of image}}{\text{size of real object}}$$

.... mm
[2]

2.2 What is the length of one plant cell in micrometres (µm)?

.... µm
[1]

2.3 How do magnification and resolution compare between electron and light microscopes?

....

....
[2]

2.4 Explain how electron microscopy has increased understanding of subcellular structures.

....

....
[2]

[Total 7 marks]

Topic B1 — Cell Biology

More on Microscopy

1   A student wants to use a light microscope to view a sample of onion cells.   *Grade 4-6*

1.1   The student adds a drop of iodine stain to her sample.
       Which statement best describes when a stain might be used to view a sample of tissue?
       Tick **one** box.

       ☐ When the specimen is too thick for light to pass through.

       ☐ When the specimen is colourless.

       ☐ When there aren't many sub-cellular structures present in the cells.

       ☐ When a cover slip is not being used.

       [1]

       Figure 1 shows a diagram of the light microscope that the student plans to use.

1.2   The three different objective lenses are labelled in **Figure 1** with
       their magnification. Which lens should the student select first when
       viewing her cells?

       ....
       [1]

       Figure 1

1.3   After she has selected the objective lens, she looks down the
       eyepiece and uses the adjustment knobs. Describe the purpose
       of the adjustment knobs.

       ....

       ....

       ....
       [1]

       × 10

       × 40

       × 4

1.4   The student wants to see the cells at a greater magnification.
       Describe the steps that she should take.

       ....

       ....

       ....
       [2]

1.5   After she has viewed the cells, she wants to produce a scientific drawing of them.
       Her teacher has advised her to use clear, unbroken lines to draw the structures she can see.
       Give **two** other ways in which she can ensure she produces an accurate and useful drawing.

       1. ....

       2. ....
       [2]

       [Total 7 marks]

Cell Differentiation and Specialisation

Different types of cell have different structures that help them carry out specific functions.
Draw arrows below to match up each type of plant cell with its structure and function.

Plant cell

root hair cell

xylem

phloem

Structure and Function

Very few subcellular structures and holes in the end cell walls allow dissolved sugars to move from one cell to the next.

Lots of chloroplasts for absorption of sunlight.

Cells that are hollow in the centre and have no end cell walls form a continuous tube for transporting water from roots to leaves.

Long finger-like projection increases surface area for absorption of water.

---

1   As an organism develops, some of its cells develop different structures and change into different types of cells. This allows the cells to carry out specific functions. What is this process called? Tick **one** box.

⬜ mitosis   ⬜ adaptation   ⬜ differentiation   ⬜ specialisation

[Total 1 mark]

---

2   Sperm cells are specialised to help them achieve their function. **Figure 1** shows the structure of a sperm cell.

Figure 1

lots of mitochondria   streamlined head

long tail   head contains enzymes

2.1 What is the function of a sperm cell?

....

[1]

2.2 Explain how the structure of a sperm cell helps it to achieve its function.
     Use **Figure 1** to help you.

....

....

....

....

[4]

[Total 5 marks]

Topic B1 — Cell Biology

Chromosomes and Mitosis

1   **Figure 1** shows different stages of the cell cycle.

Figure 1

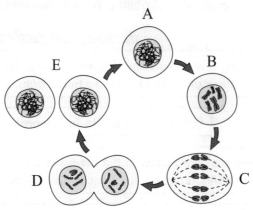

1.1   Label the chromosomes on cell B.

[1]

1.2   Name the chemical molecule that chromosomes are made of.

....

[1]

1.3   Cell A is preparing to divide. What is happening to the cell?
Tick **two** boxes.

☐ The nucleus
is dividing.   ☐ The number of subcellular
structures is increasing.   ☐ The chromosomes
are splitting.

☐ The cytoplasm
is dividing.   ☐ The chromosomes
are doubling.

[2]

1.4   Describe what is happening to cell D.

....

....

[2]

1.5   How do the two cells produced at stage E compare to parent cell A?
Tick **one** box.

☐ They are genetically different.

☐ They are genetically similar.

☐ They are genetically identical.

[1]

[Total 7 marks]

Exam Practice Tip

In the exam, you might be asked to interpret what's going on in photos of real cells undergoing mitosis. Don't panic
if the cells themselves don't look familiar — the main thing you have to look at is what the chromosomes are doing.

Topic B1 — Cell Biology

Stem Cells

1 Stem cells can be found in the growing areas of plants. *(Grade 4-6)*

1.1 What are these growing areas of a plant called?
Tick **one** box.

☐ cloning zones   ☐ meristems   ☐ leaves   ☐ mesophyll layers

[1]

1.2 You can produce cloned plants from plant stem cells.
Describe **three** benefits of producing cloned plants from stem cells.

....

....

....

[3]

[Total 4 marks]

2 Stem cells can be extracted from bone marrow and used to grow different types of cells. **Figure 1** illustrates this process. *(Grade 6-7)*

Figure 1

1. Stem cells extracted from bone marrow.

2. Stem cells cloned in culture medium.

3. Different cell types are produced.

muscle cells

nerve cells

red blood cells

white blood cells

2.1 Which of these statements about stem cells is correct? Tick **one** box.

☐ Stem cells are extracted from bone marrow because they are dangerous.

☐ Stems cells are differentiated cells.

☐ Stem cells can be found in every organ of the body.

☐ Stem cells can differentiate into many types of body cell.

[1]

2.2 Why are the stem cells cloned?

....

[1]

2.3 Why can't all body cells be used to grow different types of cell?

....

....

[1]

The technique shown in **Figure 1** could be used to produce cells for some medical treatments.

2.4 Besides bone marrow, where else can stem cells for medical treatments be obtained from?

....
[1]

2.5 Name **one** medical condition that may be helped by treatment using stem cells.

....
[1]

2.6 Give **one** potential risk of using stem cells in medical treatments.

....
[1]

[Total 6 marks]

3 **Figure 2** shows the process of therapeutic cloning. (Grade 7-9)

Figure 2

body cell

nucleus fused with empty egg cell

egg cell

nucleus removed from egg cell

embryo

stem cells

3.1 Describe what therapeutic cloning is.

....
[1]

3.2 Explain the benefit of using stem cells produced by therapeutic cloning for medical treatments compared to stem cells from a donor.

....

....
[2]

Therapeutic cloning involves creating an embryo, from which the stem cells for treatment are sourced. For this reason, some people are against using therapeutic cloning.

3.3* Discuss the ethical issues surrounding the use of embryonic stem cells in medicine and research.

....

....

....

....

....
[4]

[Total 7 marks]

Exam Practice Tip

If you're asked to write about social or ethical issues on a topic in your exam, it's a good idea to write down different points of view, so that you give a well-balanced answer. You don't have to agree with the opinions you write about.

Topic B1 — Cell Biology

Diffusion

The diagram on the right shows three cells. The carbon dioxide concentration inside each cell is shown. Draw arrows between the cells to show in which directions the carbon dioxide will diffuse.

carbon dioxide concentration = 0.2%   carbon dioxide concentration = 1.5%

carbon dioxide concentration = 3.0% ← cell

1 Which of these molecules is not able to diffuse through a cell membrane? Tick **one** box.

☐ protein   ☐ oxygen   ☐ glucose   ☐ water

[Total 1 mark]

2 A scientist investigated the diffusion of ammonia along a glass tube. **Figure 1** shows the apparatus she used.

Figure 1

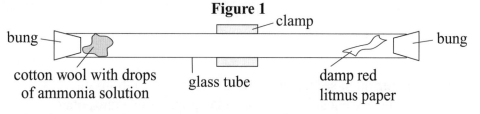

bung   clamp   bung

cotton wool with drops   glass tube   damp red
of ammonia solution   litmus paper

When the ammonia reaches the end of the tube, the litmus paper changes colour. The scientist timed how long this colour change took at five different concentrations of ammonia. **Table 1** shows her results.

Table 1

Concentration of ammonia (number of drops)	1	2	3	4	5
Time (s)	46	35	28	19	12

2.1 Define diffusion in terms of the particles of a gas.

....

....

[3]

2.2 What do the results in **Table 1** show about the effect of concentration on the rate of diffusion?

....

[1]

2.3 State **two** factors, other than concentration gradient, that affect the rate of diffusion into a cell.

....

....

[2]

2.4 Suggest how the scientist could increase the precision of her results.

....

[1]

[Total 7 marks]

Topic B1 — Cell Biology

Osmosis

1 Osmosis is a form of diffusion. (Grade 4-6)

1.1 Define osmosis.

....

....

....

[3]

1.2 In which of these is osmosis occurring? Tick **one** box.

☐ A plant is absorbing water from the soil.

☐ Sugar is being taken up into the blood from the gut.

☐ Water is evaporating from a leaf.

☐ Oxygen is entering the blood from the lungs.

[1]

[Total 4 marks]

PRACTICAL

2 A student did an experiment to see the effect of different salt solutions on pieces of potato. He cut five equal-sized rectangular chips from a raw potato and determined the mass of each chip. Each chip was placed in a beaker containing a different concentration of salt solution. The mass of each chip was measured again after 24 hours. The results are shown in **Table 1**. (Grade 6-7)

Table 1

Beaker	1	2	3	4	5
Concentration of salt solution (%)	0	1	2	5	10
Mass of potato chip at start of experiment (g)	5.70	5.73	5.71	5.75	5.77
Mass of potato chip after 24 hours (g)	6.71	6.58	6.27	5.46	4.63

2.1 Explain why it is important that all the potato pieces come from the same potato.

....

[1]

2.2 Calculate the percentage change in mass after 24 hours for the potato chip in beaker 2.

.... %

[2]

2.3 The student wanted to find a solution that would not cause the mass of the chip to change. Suggest what concentration of salt solution the student should try.

....

[1]

[Total 4 marks]

Active Transport

1   Sugar molecules can be absorbed from the gut into the blood by active transport.   Grade 4-6

1.1   Define active transport.

....

....

[1]

1.2   State how sugar molecules are used inside cells.

....

[1]

1.3   Which of these statements about active transport is correct? Tick **one** box.

☐   It is the way in which oxygen enters the blood from the lungs.

☐   It can only occur down a concentration gradient.

☐   It needs energy from respiration.

[1]

[Total 3 marks]

2   Plants absorb mineral ions from the soil by active transport.   Grade 6-7

2.1   Explain why plants need mineral ions.

....

[1]

2.2   Explain why plants are not able to rely on diffusion to absorb mineral ions from the soil.

....

....

[2]

2.3   State **two** ways in which active transport differs from diffusion.

....

....

[2]

2.4   Describe the function and structure of the root hair cells of a plant.
      Include details of how the structure of the root hair cell helps it to carry out its function.

....

....

....

....

[3]

[Total 8 marks]

Topic B1 — Cell Biology

Exchange Surfaces

Place the following organisms in order according to their surface area to volume ratio. Number the boxes 1 to 4, with 1 being the smallest and 4 being the largest.

☐ Bacterium   ☐ Tiger   ☐ Domestic cat   ☐ Blue whale

1 Give **four** features of an effective gas exchange surface in an animal.   Grade 4-6

....

....

....

....

[Total 4 marks]

2 A student was investigating the effect of size on the uptake of substances by diffusion. He cut different sized cubes of agar containing universal indicator and placed them in beakers of acid. The student timed how long it took for the acid to diffuse through to the centre of each cube (and so completely change the colour of the agar).   Grade 7-9

Table 1 shows the relationship between the surface area and volume of the agar cubes.

Table 1

Cube size (cm)	Surface area (cm²)	Volume (cm³)	Simple ratio
2 × 2 × 2	24	8	3:1
3 × 3 × 3	**X**	**Y**	2:1
5 × 5 × 5	150	125	**Z** : 1

2.1 Calculate the values of X and Y in **Table 1**.

X = ... cm²

Y = ... cm³

[2]

2.2 Calculate the value of Z.

Z = ...

[1]

2.3 Predict which cube took the longest to change colour. Give **one** reason for your answer.

Cube ....

Reason ....

[1]

[Total 4 marks]

Topic B1 — Cell Biology

Exchanging Substances

1 **Figure 1** shows an alveolus in the lungs.

Grade 4-6

Figure 1

1.1 Name gases A and B.

A ....

B ....

[2]

1.2 By what process do these gases move across the membrane?

....

[1]

1.3 State which feature of the lungs gives them:

a short diffusion pathway ....

a large surface area ....

[2]

[Total 5 marks]

2 Emphysema is a disease that weakens and breaks down the walls of the alveoli.

Grade 6-7

A person with emphysema may suffer from lower energy levels during physical exercise. Suggest and explain the cause of this symptom.

....

....

....

....

[Total 3 marks]

3 Describe and explain how the structure of the small intestine is adapted for absorbing the products of digestion.

Grade 6-7

....

....

....

....

....

....

....

....

[Total 6 marks]

Exam Practice Tip

It may seem obvious, but if you're asked to explain how the structure of something relates to its function, don't just dive straight in and rattle off what it looks like. First, focus on the function being asked about, then pick out the individual structures that help to do that function and for each structure, make sure you give a clear explanation of how it helps.

Topic B1 — Cell Biology

More on Exchanging Substances

1 Leaves are adapted for gas exchange. **Figure 1** shows the cross-section of a leaf.

Grade
4-6

1.1 Name the channels labelled X.

....
[1]

1.2 Describe the movement of gases into and out of the leaf.

....

....

....
[3]

1.3 Suggest the purpose of the air spaces in the leaf.

....

....
[1]

[Total 5 marks]

Figure 1

— air space

— X

2 **Figure 2** shows a diagram of a fish gill, which is a gas exchange surface.

Grade
6-7

2.1 How do gill filaments increase the
efficiency of the gas exchange surface?

....

....
[1]

Figure 2

arteries — — lamellae

— gill filament

2.2 What is the purpose of the lamellae?

....
[1]

2.3 Describe one other feature of an efficient gas exchange surface that is present in **Figure 2**.

....
[1]

The number and length of gill filaments differ between types of fish.
2.4 Describe the differences in the gill filaments you would expect between
a fast-moving fish and a slow-moving fish.

....
[1]

2.5 Explain why you would expect to see these differences.

....

....
[2]

[Total 6 marks]

Cell Organisation

Warm-Up

Number the boxes 1 to 4 to put the body components in order of size from smallest to largest, 1 being the smallest and 4 being the largest.

☐ Organ system   ☐ Tissue   ☐ Cell   ☐ Organ

1 The human digestive system is an example of an organ system. (Grade 4-6)

1.1 **Figure 1** shows part of the digestive system.

Figure 1

Name organs X, Y and Z.

X: ....

Y: ....

Z: ....

[3]

1.2 What is meant by the term 'organ system'?

....

....

[1]

1.3 Organ systems contain multiple types of tissue.
What is a tissue?

....

....

[1]

1.4 What is the role of the digestive system?

....

[1]

1.5 The stomach is an organ that is part of the digestive system.
What is an organ?

....

....

[1]

[Total 7 marks]

Enzymes

1 Enzymes are biological catalysts. They increase the rate of biological reactions. **Figure 1** shows a typical enzyme.

Figure 1

1.1 Name the part of the enzyme labelled X.

....

[1]

1.2 Explain the function of part X in the action of an enzyme in a chemical reaction.

....

[1]

[Total 2 marks]

2 **Figure 2** shows how temperature affects the rate of a reaction when catalysed by two different enzymes. Enzyme A is from a species of bacteria found in a hot thermal vent and Enzyme B is from a species of bacteria found in soil.

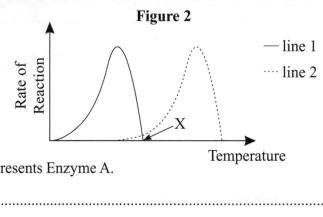

2.1 Suggest which line represents Enzyme A.

....

[1]

2.2 Explain your answer to 2.1.

....

....

....

[3]

2.3 Describe and explain what is happening at point X on the graph.

....

....

....

[4]

[Total 8 marks]

Investigating Enzymatic Reactions

PRACTICAL

1   The enzyme amylase is involved in the breakdown of starch into simple sugars.

A student investigated the effect of pH on the activity of amylase in starch solution. Amylase and starch solution were added to test tubes X, Y and Z. A different buffer solution was added to each test tube. Each buffer solution had a different pH value, as shown in **Figure 1**. Spotting tiles were prepared with a drop of iodine solution in each well. Iodine solution is a browny-orange colour but it turns blue-black in the presence of starch.

Figure 1

Test tube	pH
X	4
Y	6
Z	11

Every 30 seconds a drop of the solution from each of the test tubes was added to a separate well on a spotting tile. The resulting colour of the solution in the well was recorded as shown in **Figure 2**.

Figure 2

Time (s)	30	60	90	120	150
Tube X	Blue-black	Blue-black	Blue-black	Browny-orange	Browny-orange
Tube Y	Blue-black	Browny-orange	Browny-orange	Browny-orange	Browny-orange
Tube Z	Blue-black	Blue-black	Blue-black	Blue-black	Blue-black

1.1   State the pH at which the rate of reaction was greatest. Explain your answer.

....

....

....

                                                                     [2]

1.2   Suggest an explanation for the results in tube **Z**.

....

....

                                                                      [1]

1.3   In any experiment, it is important to control the variables that are not being tested. State how the student could control the temperature in the test tubes.

....

                                                                      [1]

1.4   Give **two** other variables that should be controlled in this experiment.

1. ....

2. ....

                                                                      [2]

1.5   The student repeated her experiment at pH 7 and got the same results as she got for her experiment at pH 6. Describe how she could improve her experiment to find whether the reaction is greatest at pH 6 or 7.

....

....

                                                                      [1]

[Total 7 marks]

Topic B2 — Organisation

Enzymes and Digestion

The diagram on the right shows some of the organs in the digestive system. Lipases and proteases are examples of digestive enzymes.

Write an 'L' on the organs that produce lipases and write a 'P' on the organs that produce proteases.

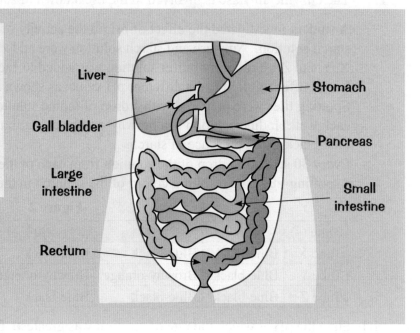

Liver

Gall bladder

Large intestine

Rectum

Stomach

Pancreas

Small intestine

1　Amylase is a digestive enzyme. Grade 4-6

1.1 Which group of digestive enzymes does amylase belong to?
Tick **one** box.

☐ Carbohydrases　　☐ Lipases　　☐ Proteases

[1]

1.2 What is the product of the reaction catalysed by amylase?
Tick **one** box.

☐ Sugars　　☐ Amino acids　　☐ Glycerol　　☐ Fatty acids

[1]

[Total 2 marks]

2　The process of digestion relies on the action of many different types of digestive enzyme. Grade 4-6

2.1 Describe the role of digestive enzymes in the process of digestion.

....

....

....

[2]

2.2 Give **two** ways in which the products of digestion can be used by the body.

....

....

[2]

[Total 4 marks]

Topic B2 — Organisation

3 Bile plays an important role in the digestive system. **(Grade 6-7)**

3.1 Name the organ where bile is produced and the organ where it is stored.

Produced ....   Stored ....

[2]

3.2 Describe **two** functions of bile and for each one explain why it is important.

....

....

....

....

....

....

[4]

[Total 6 marks]

4* Different types of food molecule are broken down by different digestive enzymes. Using your knowledge of digestive enzymes and where they are produced in the body, fully outline the processes involved in the digestion of a meal containing carbohydrates, proteins and lipids. **(Grade 7-9)**

....

....

....

....

....

....

....

....

....

....

....

....

....

....

....

[Total 6 marks]

Topic B2 — Organisation

Food Tests

Draw lines to connect the tests on the left with the biological molecules that they identify.

Biuret test   Benedict's test   Lipids   Proteins

Sudan III test   Iodine test   Starch   Reducing sugars

1* A student is analysing the nutrient content of egg whites.

Fully describe an investigation that the student could carry out to find out if protein is present in a sample of the egg whites.

....

....

....

....

....

....

....

....

[Total 6 marks]

2 A student was given test tubes containing the following glucose concentrations: 0 M, 0.02 M, 0.1 M, 1 M. The test tubes were not labelled and he was asked to perform tests to determine which test tube contained which glucose solution.

2.1 Describe the test he could carry out to try and distinguish between the glucose solutions.

....

....

....

[3]

2.2 **Table 1** shows the substance observed in the test tubes following his tests. Complete the table to show which glucose solution (0 M, 0.02 M, 0.1 M, 1 M) each test tube contained.

Table 1	Tube 1	Tube 2	Tube 3	Tube 4
substance observed	yellow precipitate	blue solution	red precipitate	green precipitate
glucose concentration (M)	....	....	....	....

[1]

[Total 4 marks]

Topic B2 — Organisation

The Lungs

Use the words on the right to correctly fill in the gaps in the passage. You don't have to use every word, but each word can only be used once.

When you breathe in, air flows through a series of tubes, including the trachea and the .... The .... are where gas exchange takes place. Gas exchange .... the blood and allows the removal of .... from the body.

oxygenates

arteries   alveoli

carbon dioxide

bronchi   oxygen

deoxygenates

1   **Figure 1** shows the human respiratory system.   Grade 4-6

Figure 1

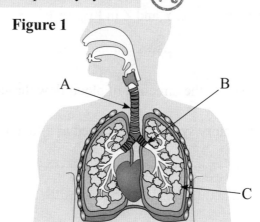

1.1   Name the parts labelled A, B and C in **Figure 1**.

A ....   B ....   C ....
[3]

Figure 2 shows a close-up of part C from **Figure 1**.

Figure 2

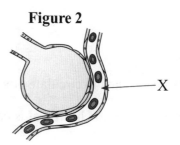

1.2   Name the structure labelled X in **Figure 2**.

....
[1]

1.3   Describe the role that structure X plays in gas exchange in the lungs.

....

....

....

....
[4]

[Total 8 marks]

Topic B2 — Organisation

Circulatory System — The Heart

1 Humans have a double circulatory system. The heart pumps blood around the body through a network of veins and arteries. **Figure 1** shows a diagram of the heart.

Figure 1

1.1 Name the parts of the heart labelled X, Y and Z in **Figure 1**.

X .... Y .... Z ....
[3]

1.2 Draw arrows on **Figure 1** to show the direction of blood flow through the right side of the heart.
[1]

1.3 Explain why the human circulatory system is described as a 'double circulatory system'.

....

....

....

....

....
[3]

[Total 7 marks]

2 The heart beats to circulate blood around the body.

2.1 Describe how the heartbeat is controlled.

....

....
[2]

2.2 Atrial fibrillation is a condition where the heartbeat is irregular. It is caused by problems with the heart's ability to control its own beat. Suggest how atrial fibrillation could be treated.

....

....

....
[2]

[Total 4 marks]

Topic B2 — Organisation

Circulatory System — Blood Vessels

1   Blood is carried around the body in blood vessels.
Different types of blood vessel perform different functions.

Grade
6-7

Figure 1 shows the three types of blood vessel.

Figure 1

A   B   C

1.1   Which of these blood vessels, A, B or C is an artery? Tick **one** box.

☐ A   ☐ B   ☐ C

[1]

1.2   The blood in arteries flows under high pressure.
Explain how arteries are adapted to perform their function.

....

....

....

[2]

1.3   Name the type of blood vessel that has valves.

....

[1]

1.4   Why does the blood vessel named in 1.3 have valves?

....

....

[1]

1.5   Explain why the walls of capillaries are only one cell thick.
Refer to their function in your answer.

....

....

....

....

....

[2]

[Total 7 marks]

Topic B2 — Organisation

Circulatory System — Blood

1 Blood is made up of several different components, including white blood cells, red blood cells and platelets.

Grade 7-9

1.1 Some diseases affect the body's ability to produce enough white blood cells.
Suggest why people with these diseases are more likely to experience frequent infections.

....

[1]

1.2 Explain how white blood cells are adapted to perform their function.

....

....

....

....

[3]

1.3 Red blood cells carry oxygen from the lungs to other tissues in the body.
Explain how red blood cells are adapted for their function.

....

....

....

....

....

[3]

The components of blood can be separated by spinning them at high speed.
Figure 1 shows a tube of blood that has been separated in this way.

Figure 1

- substance X
- white blood cells and platelets
- red blood cells

1.4 Identify the substance labelled X.

....

[1]

1.5 A scientist analysing the blood sample found that it had a lower than normal concentration of platelets. Describe the structure and function of platelets.

....

....

[2]

[Total 10 marks]

Topic B2 — Organisation

Cardiovascular Disease

Use the correct words to fill in the gaps in the passage. Not all of them will be used.

pulmonary vein   blood vessels   asthma   aorta   coronary heart disease

coronary arteries   fatty acids   toxins   fatty material   cystic fibrosis

Cardiovascular disease is a term used to describe diseases of the ....

and heart. .... is an example of a cardiovascular disease.

It is caused by narrowing of the .... due to the build-up of

.... on the inside wall.

1   The coronary arteries surround the heart.
     A patient has a blockage of fatty material in a coronary artery.   *Grade 6-7*

1.1 Explain why a blockage in the coronary arteries could cause damage to the patient's heart muscle.

....

....

[2]

1.2 Suggest and describe a method of treatment that a doctor might recommend to the patient.

....

....

....

[2]

[Total 4 marks]

2   Patients with, or at risk of, developing coronary
     heart disease are sometimes prescribed statins.   *Grade 6-7*

2.1 Explain how statins prevent or slow the progression of coronary heart disease.

....

....

....

[2]

2.2 A patient is offered statins. Suggest **one** reason why he may not wish to take them.

....

....

[1]

[Total 3 marks]

3 Doctors were assessing the heart of a patient recovering from a serious heart infection.

3.1 They found that one of the valves in the heart had become leaky.
Suggest the effects this might have on blood flow through the heart and around the body.

....

....

....
[2]

3.2 Describe **one** other way that a valve might be faulty.

....
[1]

Surgeons decided to replace the faulty valve with a replacement biological valve.

3.3 What is a biological valve?

....
[1]

3.4 A mechanical valve is sometimes used in transplants instead of a biological valve.
What is a mechanical valve?

....
[1]

A second patient at the same hospital needed a heart transplant.
Heart transplants can use donor hearts or artificial hearts.

3.5 Artificial hearts are rarely used as a permanent fix.
Suggest when they are most likely to be used instead of a natural donor heart.

....

....

....
[2]

3.6 Suggest **one** advantage and **one** disadvantage of using a natural donor heart rather than an artificial heart in heart transplant operations.

Advantage ....

....

Disadvantage ....

....
[2]

[Total 9 marks]

Health and Disease

1 Ill health is often caused by communicable and non-communicable diseases. (Grade 4-6)

1.1 What is meant by the term 'communicable disease'?

....

....

[1]

1.2 List **two** factors other than disease that can cause ill health.

....

....

[2]

[Total 3 marks]

2 **Figure 1** and **Table 1** show the number of employees in five different rooms in a large office building who have had at least one common cold in the last 12 months. (Grade 6-7)

Figure 1

Number of people who have had a cold in the last 12 months (y-axis)

Room in Office (x-axis)

Table 1	Room 1	Room 2	Room 3	Room 4	Room 5	**Total**
Number of people who have had a cold in the last 12 months	10		12	11		**60**

2.1 Complete **Figure 1** and **Table 1**.

[4]

2.2 Some people have a defective immune system. Explain what effect this could have on the likelihood of a person contracting a communicable disease like the common cold.

....

....

....

[2]

[Total 6 marks]

Topic B2 — Organisation

Risk Factors for Non-Communicable Diseases

1 Substances in a person's environment can be risk factors for certain diseases. *Grade 4-6*

1.1 What is meant by a risk factor for a disease?

....

....

....

[1]

1.2 Other than substances in the environment, state **two** other types of risk factor.

....

....

[2]

1.3 Obesity is a risk factor for many different diseases.
Name **one** disease that obesity is a risk factor for.

....

[1]

[Total 4 marks]

2 A patient has been diagnosed with cardiovascular disease. *Grade 4-6*

2.1 Give **two** risk factors that might have contributed to her developing cardiovascular disease.

....

....

[2]

2.2 Suggest **two** reasons why non-communicable diseases can be financially costly.

....

....

....

....

[2]

[Total 4 marks]

Exam Practice Tip
Remember that risk factors are identified by scientists looking for correlations in data, and they don't always directly cause a disease. Sometimes, they are just related to another factor that does. It's rarely a single risk factor that leads to someone developing a disease — diseases are often caused when multiple risk factors interact with each other.

Cancer

Tumours can be benign or malignant. Draw lines to match the types of
tumour on the left with each characteristic on the right that applies to them.

Are cancerous

Malignant Tumours

Are not cancerous

Benign Tumours

Can invade neighbouring tissues

1   Some types of tumour are cancerous. **Grade 4-6**

1.1 What do tumours result from?
Tick **one** box.

☐ Rapid cell death

☐ Slow cell division

☐ Lack of cell division

☐ Uncontrolled cell division

[1]

1.2 There are many known lifestyle-related risk factors for cancer. However, not all risk factors for
cancer are related to lifestyle. Give **one** other type of risk factor for cancer.

....

[1]

[Total 2 marks]

2   Doctors found a tumour in the left lung of a patient.
They were concerned that the patient was at risk of developing secondary tumours. **Grade 6-7**

2.1 Was the tumour in the patient's lung malignant or benign?

....

[1]

2.2 Explain how a secondary tumour forms.

....

....

....

[2]

[Total 3 marks]

 ☐   ☐   ☐

Plant Cell Organisation

1 The roots, stem and leaves are involved in the transport of substances around a plant. **Grade 4-6**

1.1 What do the roots, stem and leaves of a plant form? Tick **one** box.

☐ A tissue   ☐ An organ system   ☐ An organ   ☐ A tissue system

[1]

1.2 Name **two** substances that are transported around a plant in the xylem.

....

[2]

[Total 3 marks]

2 Plants have many types of tissue, including meristem tissue. **Grade 4-6**

2.1 Name **two** sites in a plant where you would find meristem tissue.

....

....

[2]

2.2 Give **one** reason why meristem tissue is important throughout the life of the plant.

....

[1]

[Total 3 marks]

3 **Figure 1** shows a transverse section of a leaf. **Grade 6-7**

Figure 1

epidermal tissue
xylem
phloem
air space
epidermal tissue

A
B

3.1 Name the tissues labelled A and B.

A ....   B ....

[2]

3.2 Explain how the tissue labelled A is adapted for the function of photosynthesis.

....

....

....

[2]

3.3 What is the function of the air spaces?

....

[1]

[Total 5 marks]

Transpiration and Translocation

Warm-Up

Use the words below to correctly fill in the gaps in the passage.
You don't have to use every word, but each word can only be used once.

leaves   phloem   translocation   mineral ions   condensation   evaporation

roots   perspiration   xylem   transpiration   sugars   guard cells   stem

The process by which water is lost from a plant is called ....

It is caused by the .... and diffusion of water from a plant's surface,

most often from the .... Another process, called ....,

is the transport of .... from where they're made in the leaves to the rest

of the plant via the .... vessels.

1*   Describe how xylem tissue and phloem tissue work to:
   • supply water and mineral ions to all parts of a plant,
   • transport dissolved sugars around a plant.
Include details of the **structure** and **function** of the tissues involved.

(Grade 7-9)

....

....

....

....

....

....

....

....

....

....

....

....

....

[Total 6 marks]

Exam Practice Tip

It can be tricky to remember which is which when thinking of xylem and phloem. They're both pretty similar and they've both got weird names. If you're struggling to remember, keep practising this question. It will soon stick in your head.

Topic B2 — Organisation

Transpiration and Stomata

1 **Figure 1** is a drawing of a magnified image of part of the surface of a leaf

Figure 1

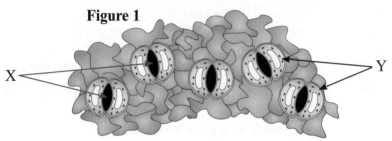

X   Y

1.1 Name the structures labelled X and the cells labelled Y in **Figure 1**.

X ....   Y ....

[2]

1.2 What is the function of the cells labelled Y?

....

....

....

[2]

[Total 4 marks]

2 **Table 1** shows the diameter of ten stomata from each of two leaves, A and B.

Table 1

Diameter of stomata (µm)	
Leaf A	Leaf B
25.2, 20.1, 18.7, 17.9, 19.1, 19.3, 22.0, 23.1, 21.8, 20.3	14.7, 12.8, 14.1, 13.2, 12.9, 11.9, 12.1, 13.4, 10.9, 11.7

2.1 Calculate the mean width of the stomata for each leaf.

Leaf A = ... µm   Leaf B = ... µm

[2]

2.2 Leaves A and B are from the same species. Which leaf do you think had its stomatal measurements taken in lower light intensity?

....

[1]

2.3 Explain your answer to 2.2.

....

....

....

[2]

[Total 5 marks]

3   An investigation was carried out to assess the rate of water uptake by a plant over a 16-hour period.

A potometer was set up and readings were taken every two hours between 00:00 and 16:00.

The rate in cm³/hour was calculated for each two-hour period.

The results are shown in **Table 2**.

Table 2

Time of day	00:00	02:00	04:00	06:00	08:00	10:00	12:00	14:00	16:00
Rate of water uptake (cm³/hour)	2.6	1.0	1.6	2.0	3.8	6.2	8.0	10.2	7.6

3.1   Complete **Figure 2** using the data displayed in **Table 2**.
   • Select a suitable scale and label for the y-axis
   • Plot the rate of water uptake in cm³/hour for all the times given in **Table 2**
   • Join the points with straight lines

Figure 2

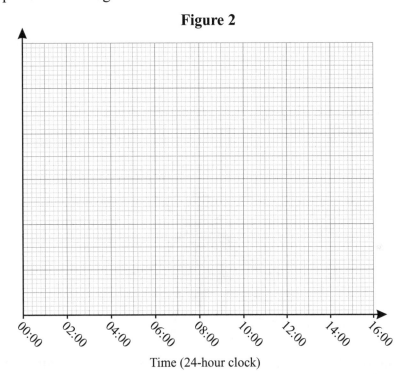

Time (24-hour clock)

Use your graph to answer 3.2 and 3.3 below.   *[4]*

3.2   Use the graph to estimate the rate of water uptake at 09:00.

....

                                                                                                            [1]

3.3   How much did the rate of water uptake increase between 06:00 and 11:00?

....

                                                                                                            [1]

3.4   Suggest **two** environmental changes that could have caused the change in water uptake between 06:00 and 14:00.

....

....

                                                                                                            [2]

                                                                                             [Total 8 marks]

Topic B2 — Organisation

Communicable Disease

1   Viruses and bacteria can both reproduce inside the human body.   (Grade 4-6)

1.1   Which of the following sentences is correct?   Tick **one** box.

☐   Both bacteria and viruses can reproduce quickly in the body.

☐   Bacteria reproduce quickly in the body, but viruses reproduce slowly.

☐   Viruses reproduce quickly in the body, but bacteria reproduce slowly.

☐   Both bacteria and viruses reproduce slowly in the body.

[1]

1.2   Viruses reproduce inside cells.   Describe what problem this can cause for the cells.

....

[1]

[Total 2 marks]

2*   **Figure 1** shows a housefly.   Houseflies are vectors because they can transmit disease to humans.   (Grade 7-9)

Figure 1

legs covered in tiny hairs

mouthparts secrete saliva

wings

faeces produced

Use information from **Figure 1** to explain how the housefly can transmit disease to humans. Include details of how the housefly can pick up pathogens and spread them to humans.

....

....

....

....

....

....

....

....

[Total 6 marks]

Viral, Fungal and Protist Diseases

Fill in the gaps in the passage about malaria. Use the words on the left.
Not all of the words will be used.

protist   breeding

vectors

        fungi

fever

        bacterium

virus

Malaria is caused by a .... Mosquitoes are the

.... that carry the malaria pathogen to humans.

Malaria causes repeating episodes of .... The spread of

malaria can be reduced by stopping the mosquitoes from ....

---

1 Measles is a highly infectious disease. **Grade 4-6**

1.1 What type of pathogen causes measles? Tick **one** box.

☐ bacterium   ☐ virus   ☐ protist   ☐ fungus

[1]

1.2 A person suffering from measles travels to work by train. Explain how, 10 days later, other people who were on the same train may also be suffering from measles.

....

....

....

[3]

1.3 Measles can be fatal if there are complications.
What can be done to prevent someone from developing measles?

....

[1]

[Total 5 marks]

2 A virus called HIV causes a disease known as AIDS. **Grade 4-6**

2.1 What type of drug can be used to control HIV?

....

[1]

2.2 What system in the body does HIV attack?

....

[1]

2.3 State **two** ways in which HIV can be spread.

....

....

[2]

[Total 4 marks]

3   The tobacco mosaic virus (TMV) is a widespread plant pathogen affecting many species of plants.   (Grade 6-7)

3.1   Name **one** species of plant that is often attacked by the tobacco mosaic virus.

....

[1]

3.2   Describe the appearance of a plant with TMV.

....

[1]

3.3   Outline why a plant affected by TMV cannot grow properly.

....

....

[1]

3.4   **Table 1** shows the mean diameter and mass of fruits from 100 healthy plants and 100 plants infected with TMV.

Table 1

	Healthy plants	Plants with TMV
Mean diameter of fruit (mm)	50	35
Mean mass of fruit (g)	95	65

Describe the effect of TMV on the diameter and mass of fruit produced in the infected plants compared to the healthy plants.

....

....

....

[2]

[Total 5 marks]

4   Rose black spot is a disease that can affect rose plants.   (Grade 6-7)

4.1   Describe the appearance of leaves that are infected with rose black spot and state what happens to these leaves.

....

....

[3]

4.2   A gardener notices that one of her rose plants is infected with rose black spot.
She is worried about the rest of her rose plants becoming infected with the fungus.
Why are the other rose plants in her garden at risk from being infected with the disease?

....

[1]

4.3   Rose black spot can be treated by removing and destroying the infected leaves and treating the rest of the plant with a fungicide. Suggest why it is important to destroy the removed leaves.

....

....

[1]

[Total 5 marks]

Bacterial Diseases and Preventing Disease

1   *Salmonella* food poisoning in humans is caused by a bacterium.   (Grade 4-6)

1.1 List **two** symptoms of *Salmonella* food poisoning.

....

....

[2]

1.2 What does the *Salmonella* bacterium produce that causes these symptoms?

....

[1]

1.3 In the UK, poultry are vaccinated against the bacterium that causes food poisoning.
Explain why it is necessary to vaccinate poultry.

....

....

....

[2]

1.4 Suggest **one** way that a person suffering from *Salmonella* food poisoning can prevent passing the disease on to someone else.

....

[1]

[Total 6 marks]

2   Gonorrhoea is a disease that can affect both men and women.   (Grade 4-6)

2.1 How is gonorrhoea spread from person to person?

....

[1]

2.2 State **two** symptoms of the disease in women.

....

....

[2]

2.3 Name the antibiotic that was originally used to treat people infected with gonorrhoea.

....

[1]

2.4 Why is the antibiotic in part 2.3 no longer effective against the bacterium that causes gonorrhoea?

....

[1]

2.5 Name **one** barrier method of contraception that prevents the spread of gonorrhoea.

....

[1]

[Total 6 marks]

Topic B3 — Infection and Response

Fighting Disease

1   The body has many features that it can use to protect itself against pathogens.   (Grade 4-6)

   1.1   Describe how the skin helps to defend the body against pathogens.

....

....

           [2]

   1.2   How do structures in the nose help to defend the body against the entry of pathogens?

....

....

           [1]

           [Total 3 marks]

2*   Describe how the human body works to defend itself against pathogens that have entered the body. Include details of the body's defences and the role of the immune system.   (Grade 6-7)

....

....

....

....

....

....

....

....

....

....

....

....

           [Total 6 marks]

Exam Practice Tip

Think carefully about 6 mark questions like the one on this page. Don't just start scribbling everything you know about the topic. Stop and think first — work out what the question is wanting you to write about, and then make sure you write enough points to bag yourself as many marks as possible. Good job you've got some practice on this page.

Topic B3 — Infection and Response

Fighting Disease — Vaccination

1 Children are often vaccinated against measles. *Grade 4-6*

1.1 What is injected into the body during a vaccination?

....

[1]

1.2 Describe what happens when a vaccine is injected into the body. Tick **one** box.

☐ Red blood cells are stimulated to produce antibodies.

☐ White blood cells are stimulated to produce antibiotics.

☐ Red blood cells are stimulated to produce antibiotics.

☐ White blood cells are stimulated to produce antibodies.

[1]

[Total 2 marks]

2 People can be vaccinated against a large number of diseases. *Grade 6-7*

2.1 If the mumps pathogen enters the body of someone who has had the mumps vaccination, why would they be unlikely to become ill with mumps?

....

[1]

2.2 A large proportion of a population is vaccinated against a particular pathogen. Suggest why the spread of the pathogen will be very much reduced.

....

....

....

[2]

[Total 3 marks]

3 When visiting some other countries, it is recommended that travellers are vaccinated against some of the serious diseases found in those countries. *Grade 7-9*

3.1 If a traveller planned to visit a country where there had been a recent outbreak of the communicable disease cholera, they might get vaccinated against cholera before they travelled. Give **two** reasons why this would be beneficial.

....

....

[2]

3.2 Some countries insist that travellers have had particular vaccinations before they are allowed to enter the country. Suggest why.

....

[1]

[Total 3 marks]

Topic B3 — Infection and Response

Fighting Disease — Drugs

1 There are many different types of drugs with different functions. **Grade 6-7**

1.1 Explain why it is difficult to develop drugs to kill viruses.

....

....

[2]

1.2 Many people suffer from sore throats caused by bacteria. Other than an antibiotic, name a type of drug that could be used to ease the symptoms of the infection.

....

[1]

1.3 Explain why the type of drug named in 1.2 would not be able to cure the bacterial infection.

....

[1]

[Total 4 marks]

2 A hospital records the number of cases of infections that are caused by antibiotic-resistant bacteria each year. The figures for three years are shown in **Table 1**. **Grade 6-7**

Table 1

Year	2013	2014	2015
No. of infections	84	102	153

2.1 What is meant by antibiotic-resistant bacteria?

....

....

[1]

2.2 Describe the trend shown in **Table 1**.

....

....

[1]

2.3 Use **Table 1** to calculate the percentage change in antibiotic resistant infections between 2013 and 2015.

.... %

[2]

[Total 4 marks]

Exam Practice Tip

When you're answering an exam question about drugs and disease, think very carefully about whether the drug kills the pathogens causing the disease (and so cures it), or whether it just helps to make the symptoms of the disease better.

Topic B3 — Infection and Response

Developing Drugs

1   New drugs have to be tested and trialled before they can be used.   Grade 4-6

1.1 List **three** things drugs must be tested for, to ensure they are safe and effective.

....

....

....

[3]

1.2 Which of the following is preclinical testing carried out on? Tick **one** box.

☐ healthy human volunteers   ☐ patients in a hospital

☐ cells, tissues and dead animals   ☐ cells, tissues and live animals

[1]

[Total 4 marks]

2   Clinical trials are always carried out on healthy volunteers before patients.   Grade 7-9

2.1 Suggest why very low doses of the drug are given at the start of clinical trials.

....

[1]

2.2 Clinical trials are often double-blind. Explain what would happen in a double-blind clinical trial.

....

....

....

[3]

2.3 Suggest why clinical trials are carried out using a double-blind method.

....

....

[1]

The final results of clinical trials cannot be published until they have been checked
by other scientists. Such checking is often referred to as peer review.

2.4 Suggest why peer review is important in these trials.

....

[1]

2.5 Suggest why it is important that the scientists who carry out the peer review have
no links to the people who carried out the original trials.

....

....

[2]

[Total 8 marks]

Topic B3 — Infection and Response

Photosynthesis and Limiting Factors

1 Photosynthesis is where energy is transferred to plants and used to make glucose. (Grade 4-6)

1.1 What is the source of energy for photosynthesis?

....

[1]

1.2 Complete the following word equation for photosynthesis.

.... + water → glucose + ...

[2]

Plants use the glucose they produce in lots of different ways, including to make a substance to strengthen cell walls.

1.3 Name the substance that plants use to strengthen cell walls.

....

[1]

1.4 Give **two** other ways that plants use the glucose produced during photosynthesis.

....

....

....

....

[2]

[Total 6 marks]

2 Photosynthesis is an endothermic reaction. Various factors affect its rate. (Grade 6-7)

2.1 Explain what is meant by an endothermic reaction.

....

[1]

2.2 Which of the following factors does not affect the rate of photosynthesis?
Tick **one** box.

☐ carbon dioxide concentration   ☐ nitrate concentration   ☐ light intensity   ☐ temperature

[1]

2.3 A lack of magnesium can cause chloroplasts not to make enough chlorophyll.
Explain what effect this would have on the rate of photosynthesis of a plant.

....

....

[2]

[Total 4 marks]

The Rate of Photosynthesis

Warm-Up

Choose from the words below to complete the sentences explaining how temperature affects the rate of photosynthesis, as shown in the graph. Some words may not be used at all.

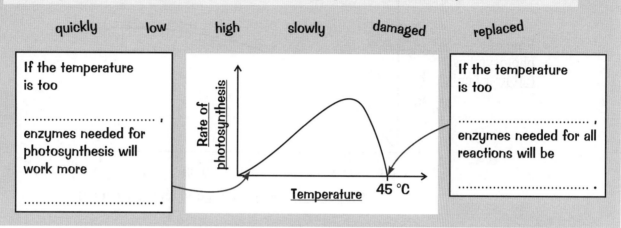

quickly   low   high   slowly   damaged   replaced

If the temperature is too

.... ,

enzymes needed for photosynthesis will work more

....

Rate of photosynthesis

Temperature   45 °C

If the temperature is too

.... ,

enzymes needed for all reactions will be

....

1   **Figure 1** shows a greenhouse. Greenhouses are used to create the ideal conditions for photosynthesis.

Grade 6-7

Figure 1

1.1 Suggest **two** ways that a farmer could improve the conditions for photosynthesis in a greenhouse. For each of the ways, explain how it affects the rate of photosynthesis.

Improvement ....

Explanation ....

....

Improvement ....

Explanation ....

....

[4]

1.2 Creating the ideal conditions in a greenhouse costs money. Explain why it may still be beneficial for the farmer to do this.

....

....

[2]

[Total 6 marks]

2   A student carried out an experiment to investigate the effect of changing the concentration of carbon dioxide on the rate of photosynthesis in a green plant. The results were plotted on the graph shown in **Figure 2**.

Figure 2

2.1   Describe the trend shown in the graph.

....

....

....

[2]

2.2   At a certain point, the CO_2 concentration is no longer limiting the rate of photosynthesis. Suggest **two** factors that could be limiting the rate at this point.

....

....

[2]

2.3   In the space below, sketch a graph to show how light intensity affects the rate of photosynthesis.

[2]

[Total 6 marks]

3 A student was investigating the effect of light intensity on the rate of photosynthesis in a water plant. She set up the experiment as shown in **Figure 3**.

Figure 3

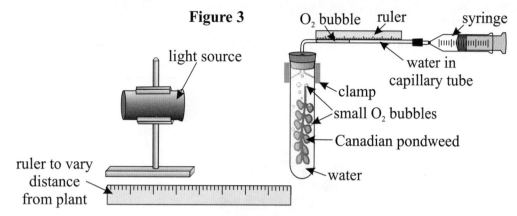

3.1 Predict what will happen to the volume of gas produced when the light is moved closer to the pondweed.

....

[1]

3.2 The formula $1/distance^2$ can be used as a measure of light intensity. It's called the inverse square law. Use the inverse square law to calculate the light intensity when the lamp is 20 cm from the pondweed.

light intensity = ... arbitrary units

[2]

3.3* Suggest how the student could adapt the experiment shown in **Figure 3** to investigate the effect of temperature on the rate of photosynthesis. Include details of the variables that should be controlled.

....

....

....

....

....

....

....

....

[6]

[Total 9 marks]

Exam Practice Tip

There's a lot to learn about limiting factors and the rate of photosynthesis. It's a good idea to practise drawing the graphs to show the effect of light intensity, carbon dioxide concentration and temperature on the rate of photosynthesis. You should also make sure you're able to interpret the graphs too, including those with more than one factor involved.

Respiration and Metabolism

1 Respiration is a reaction carried out by all living organisms. It transfers energy from an organism's food to their cells.

Grade 6-7

1.1 Name the type of reaction where energy is transferred to the environment.

....

[1]

Figure 1 shows a gull.

Figure 1

1.2 Give **three** examples of how a gull uses the energy transferred by respiration.

....

....

....

[3]

[Total 4 marks]

2 Metabolism is the sum of all of the reactions that happen in a cell or the body. Metabolism includes reactions that make molecules.

Grade 6-7

2.1 Some metabolic reactions involve using glucose molecules to make other molecules. Name a molecule made from glucose in plants, and a molecule made from glucose in animals.

Plants ....

Animals ....

[2]

2.2 Describe the components of a lipid molecule.

....

....

[2]

2.3 Briefly describe how protein molecules are formed.

....

....

[2]

2.4 Metabolism also involves breaking down molecules. What is excess protein broken down to produce?

....

[1]

[Total 7 marks]

Topic B4 — Bioenergetics

Aerobic and Anaerobic Respiration

Draw lines to match up each process on the left with its correct description on the right.

| Aerobic respiration |
| Anaerobic respiration |
| Fermentation |

| Respiration without oxygen. |
| Respiration using oxygen. |

1   An experiment was set up using two sealed beakers, each with a carbon dioxide monitor attached. The set up is shown in **Figure 1**.

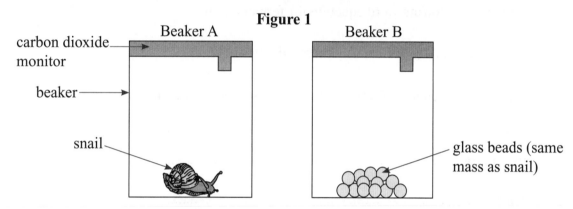

Figure 1

The percentage (%) of carbon dioxide in the air in both beakers was measured at the start of the experiment and again after 2 hours. The results are shown in **Table 1**.

Table 1

Time (hours)	% carbon dioxide in the air	
	Beaker A	Beaker B
0	0.04	0.04
2	0.10	0.04

1.1 Suggest **one** ethical consideration that must be taken into account during this experiment.

....

[1]

1.2 Describe and explain the results for Beaker A.

....

....

[1]

1.3 Describe and explain the results for Beaker B.

....

....

[1]

48

1.4 What would have happened to the level of oxygen in Beaker A after two hours? Explain your answer.

....

....

[2]

1.5 In the experiment, Beaker B was set up in the same way as Beaker A but with glass beads instead of a snail. Suggest why Beaker B is used in the experiment.

....

....

[1]

[Total 6 marks]

2 *S. cerevisiae* is a type of yeast. It carries out fermentation. **Grade 6-7**

2.1 Complete the following word equation for fermentation.

.... → ethanol + carbon dioxide

[1]

2.2 For each of the products of fermentation in yeast, outline **one** industrial use.

Product ....

Industrial use ....

Product ....

Industrial use ....

[2]

[Total 3 marks]

3 **Figure 2** shows a muscle cell.
Compare aerobic respiration and anaerobic respiration in muscle cells. **Grade 6-7**

Figure 2

....

....

....

....

....

....

[Total 3 marks]

Topic B4 — Bioenergetics

Exercise

Warm-Up

Choose from the words on the right to complete the sentences about exercise. Some words may not be used at all.

carbon dioxide   oxygen   aerobically   lactic acid   urea   oxygen debt   muscles

During exercise your .... may respire anaerobically resulting in an

.... This is the amount of extra .... your body

needs to react with the build up of .... and remove it from cells.

1 A student was investigating the effect of exercise on his own breathing rate. He counted his number of breaths per minute before, during and after a period of exercise. He repeated his experiment another two times. The results are shown in **Table 1** below.

Table 1

Breathing rate (number of breaths per minute)			
Before exercise	During exercise	One minute after exercise	Five minutes after exercise
11	16	15	12
12	15	14	11
11	15	14	12
Mean 11	15	14	

1.1 Calculate the mean breathing rate five minutes after exercise.

Mean = ... breaths per minute

[1]

1.2 Describe and explain how the student's breathing rate changed during exercise compared to before exercise, as shown in **Table 1**.

....

....

....

[3]

1.3 Describe and explain how the student's breathing rate changed after exercise compared to during exercise, as shown in **Table 1**.

....

....

....

....

[5]

1.4 Give **two** other variables that the student could have measured which would have shown the same trend as breathing rate during exercise.

....

....

[2]

[Total 11 marks]

2   **Figure 1** below shows the amount of lactic acid in an athlete's body before, during and after some vigorous exercise.

Grade 7-9

Figure 1

2.1 The amount of lactic acid increases from 20 au to 80 au across the duration of the exercise period. Work out the percentage change in lactic acid during this time.

Percentage change = ...%

[2]

2.2 Explain why there was an increase in lactic acid during the exercise period.

....

....

....

[3]

2.3 What physical effects does a long period of vigorous exercise have on muscles?

....

....

[2]

2.4 The amount of lactic acid in the athlete's body decreases between 20 and 60 minutes. Explain how this lactic acid is cleared from the body.

....

....

[2]

[Total 9 marks]

Topic B4 — Bioenergetics

Homeostasis

1   Human blood pressure is maintained by a homeostatic control system.   Grade 6-7

1.1   What is homeostasis?

....

....

....

[2]

1.2   Why are homeostatic control systems important in the body?

....

[1]

1.3   Blood pressure is monitored by sensors in the blood vessels.
Which component of a homeostatic control system senses blood pressure? Tick **one** box.

☐ coordination centre   ☐ receptor   ☐ stimulus   ☐ effector

[1]

1.4   Outline the stages in the negative feedback mechanism when blood pressure becomes too high.

....

....

....

[3]

[Total 7 marks]

2   A person's skin temperature was measured over a 50 minute period.   Grade 6-7

During that time, the person began exercising. They then returned to a resting state before the end of the investigation. **Figure 1** shows the change in the person's skin temperature over the 50 minutes.

Figure 1

[Graph showing Temperature (°C) on y-axis from 34.0 to 35.5 against Time (minutes) on x-axis from 0 to 50]

2.1   Suggest the time at which the person began exercising.

....

[1]

2.2   Calculate the rate at which the temperature increased between 20 and 30 minutes.

Rate = ...°C/min

[2]

[Total 3 marks]

The Nervous System

1   **Figure 1** shows part of the human nervous system.   (Grade 4-6)

1.1   Name the structures labelled **X** and **Y** on **Figure 1**.

X   ....

Y   ....

[2]

1.2   Which part of the nervous system do structures **X** and **Y** form?

....

[1]

1.3   What is the role of the part of the nervous system formed by
structures **X** and **Y**?

....

....

[1]

[Total 4 marks]

Figure 1

2   Multicellular organisms such as humans have a nervous system.   (Grade 6-7)

2.1   What is the function of the nervous system in humans?

....

....

[2]

2.2   Receptor cells in the eye are sensitive to light.
For a nervous system response in the eye, state whether each of the following features
is a stimulus, a coordinator or a response.

Spinal cord   ....

Bright light   ....

Blinking   ....

[3]

2.3   Name the **two** main types of neurones found in humans outside the central nervous system.

....

....

[2]

2.4   Name **two** types of effector and state how they respond to nervous impulses.

....

....

[2]

[Total 9 marks]

Topic B5 — Homeostasis and Response

Synapses and Reflexes

1 Which of the following sentences is correct? Tick **one** box. (Grade 4-6)

☐ Reflex reactions are slow and under conscious control.

☐ Reflex reactions are slow and automatic.

☐ Reflex reactions are rapid and automatic.

☐ Reflex reactions are rapid and under conscious control.

[Total 1 mark]

2 **Figure 1** shows a reflex arc. (Grade 4-6)

Figure 1

2.1 Name structures **X**, **Y** and **Z**.

X ....

Y ....

Z ....

[3]

2.2 In the reflex arc shown in **Figure 1**, name:

the stimulus ....

the coordinator ....

the effector ....

[3]

2.3 Structure **A** is the junction between two neurones. Name structure **A**.

....

[1]

2.4 How is a nerve signal transmitted across this junction?

....

[1]

[Total 8 marks]

Topic B5 — Homeostasis and Response

PRACTICAL Investigating Reaction Time

1 Stimulants, like caffeine, increase the rate at which nerve impulses travel. An investigation was carried out to assess the impact of different caffeinated drinks on reaction time.

The investigation involved measuring reaction time using a ruler drop test. In this test, a ruler is held above a student's outstretched hand by another person. The ruler is then dropped without warning and the student catches the ruler as quickly as possible. The distance down the ruler where the student caught it is used to calculate their reaction time in seconds (s).
Three different students (Students **1** to **3**) consumed a different caffeinated drink — each one contained a different amount of caffeine. Each student then undertook three ruler drop tests. The results are shown in the table below.

1.1 Calculate the mean reaction time for Student **2** and Student **3**.

Student **2** = ... s

Student **3** = ... s

[2]

	Reaction time (s)		
	Student 1	Student 2	Student 3
Test 1	0.09	0.16	0.20
Test 2	0.10	0.13	0.22
Test 3	0.43	0.15	0.19
Mean	0.21		

1.2 Identify the anomalous result in the table.

....

[1]

1.3 The students' reaction time without any caffeine was **not** measured. Explain why it should have been included in the investigation to assess the effect of each caffeinated drink.

....

....

....

[2]

1.4 Explain why the results of this investigation can't be used to **compare** the effect of the three different caffeinated drinks on reaction time.

....

....

[2]

1.5 An alternative version of the investigation was carried out. This time, the effect of a set quantity of caffeine on the reaction times of different individuals was investigated. Reaction times of three different students were measured, both before and after the consumption of caffeine.
Give **three** variables that should have been controlled in this investigation.

....

....

....

[3]

[Total 10 marks]

The Endocrine System

1 The endocrine system is a collection of glands in the body that secrete hormones. Grade 4-6

1.1 Which of the following statements about glands is correct? Tick **one** box.

☐ Glands secrete hormones directly into cells.

☐ Glands secrete hormones directly into tissues.

☐ Glands secrete hormones directly into the blood.

☐ Glands secrete hormones directly into organs.

[1]

1.2 Which of the following statements best describes hormones?
Tick **one** box.

☐ Hormones are tissues.   ☐ Hormones are chemical molecules.

☐ Hormones are cells.   ☐ Hormones are enzymes.

[1]

1.3 State **two** ways in which the effects of the endocrine system differ from the nervous system.

....

....

[2]

[Total 4 marks]

2 **Figure 1** shows the positions of some glands in the human body. Grade 4-6

2.1 Name glands A to E in **Figure 1**.

Figure 1

A ....

B ....

C ....

D ....

E ....

[5]

The 'master gland' secretes several hormones
into the blood in response to body conditions.

2.2 What is the name of the 'master gland'?

....

[1]

2.3 What is the function of the hormones released by the 'master gland'?

....

....

[2]

[Total 8 marks]

Controlling Blood Glucose

1 The concentration of glucose in the blood is controlled by hormones. *(Grade 4-6)*

1.1 Which gland in the human body monitors and controls blood glucose concentration?
Tick **one** box.

☐ pancreas ☐ pituitary gland ☐ thyroid ☐ testis

[1]

1.2 Which hormone is produced when blood glucose concentration becomes too high?

....

[1]

1.3 Describe what happens to excess glucose in the blood.

....

....

[2]

[Total 4 marks]

2 Diabetes exists in two different forms, Type 1 and Type 2. *(Grade 6-7)*

2.1 What causes Type 1 diabetes?

....

[1]

2.2 What is the defining characteristic of Type 1 diabetes?

....

[1]

2.3 Type 1 diabetes is treated with insulin injections.
Suggest **one** factor that might affect the amount of insulin injected by a patient.

....

[1]

2.4 What causes Type 2 diabetes?

....

[1]

2.5 Give **two** treatments that a doctor would recommend for Type 2 diabetes.

....

....

[2]

2.6 Give a risk factor for Type 2 diabetes.

....

[1]

[Total 7 marks]

3 In an experiment, the blood glucose concentration of a person without diabetes was recorded at regular intervals in a 90 minute time period. Fifteen minutes into the experiment, a glucose drink was given. **Figure 1** shows the results of the experiment.

Figure 1

3.1 Explain what is happening to the blood glucose concentration between 15 and 60 minutes.

....

....

....
[3]

3.2 Name the hormone being released by the pancreas at point **X** on the graph.

....
[1]

3.3 Describe the effect that hormone **X** has on the blood glucose concentration.

....
[1]

3.4 Explain how hormone **X** causes this effect.

....

....
[1]

3.5 Suggest how the shape of the graph would differ if the person had Type 1 diabetes.

....

....
[1]

[Total 7 marks]

Exam Practice Tip

There are a few similar-sounding names when it comes to the control of blood glucose, so make sure you've got your head around which is which (and how to spell them). You won't get the mark if, for example, you write about 'glucogen'...

Puberty and the Menstrual Cycle

1 The release of sex hormones begins at puberty. *Grade 4-6*

1.1 What is the name of the main female hormone produced in the ovary? Tick **one** box.

☐ progesterone   ☐ oestrogen   ☐ luteinising hormone   ☐ follicle stimulating hormone

[1]

1.2 What is the name of the process by which eggs are released from the ovary?

....

[1]

1.3 How often is an egg released from an ovary? Tick **one** box.

☐ Every 7 days.   ☐ Every 14 days.   ☐ Every 21 days.   ☐ Every 28 days.

[1]

1.4 Name the hormone that stimulates the release of an egg.

....

[1]

1.5 Name the hormone that stimulates sperm production in men.

....

[1]

1.6 Where in the male body is this hormone produced?

....

[1]

[Total 6 marks]

2 Four main hormones interact with each other in the control of the menstrual cycle. *Grade 6-7*

2.1 Which two hormones are involved in maintaining the uterus lining?

....

....

[2]

2.2 What is the name of the gland that secretes follicle stimulating hormone (FSH)?

....

[1]

2.3 State **two** effects of FSH during the menstrual cycle of a woman.

....

....

[2]

2.4 Which hormone stimulates the release of luteinising hormone (LH)?

....

[1]

[Total 6 marks]

Topic B5 — Homeostasis and Response

Controlling Fertility

Sort the methods of contraception into the correct places in the table.

abstinence

contraceptive injection

condom

diaphragm

plastic intrauterine device

sterilisation

contraceptive patch

Hormonal	Non-hormonal

1 Some methods of contraception use hormones to control the fertility of a woman. *(Grade 4-6)*

1.1 How is an oral contraceptive taken into the body?
Tick **one** box.

☐ As an injection.

☐ As a tablet taken by mouth.

☐ Through the skin from a patch.

[1]

1.2 How do oral contraceptives containing multiple hormones prevent pregnancy?
Tick **one** box.

☐ The hormones inhibit oestrogen production.

☐ The hormones inhibit FSH production.

☐ The hormones inhibit LH production.

[1]

1.3 The contraceptive implant is inserted under the skin of the arm.
Which hormone does it release?

....

[1]

1.4 How does the hormone released by the contraceptive implant prevent pregnancy?

....

[1]

[Total 4 marks]

2 Fertility can be controlled by non-hormonal methods of contraception. **Grade 4-6**

2.1 Name a barrier method of contraception that can be used by men.

....
[1]

2.2 Name a barrier method of contraception that can be used by women.

....
[1]

2.3 How do barrier methods of contraception prevent a woman becoming pregnant?

....
[1]

2.4 What is the name given to chemicals that kill or disable sperm?

....
[1]

2.5 A couple not wishing to have children do not want to use any form of contraception.
Suggest how they could avoid pregnancy.

....
[1]

2.6 Name a surgical method of controlling fertility that can be carried out in both men and women.

....
[1]

2.7 Name a barrier method of contraception that protects against sexually transmitted infections.

....
[1]

[Total 7 marks]

3 A woman is considering which contraceptive to use. **Grade 7-9**

3.1 Suggest **one** advantage of choosing the contraceptive injection over the contraceptive pill.

....
[1]

3.2 Suggest **one** disadvantage of choosing the contraceptive injection over the contraceptive pill.

....
[1]

3.3 Suggest **one** advantage of choosing a barrier method of contraception over a hormonal
contraceptive.

....
[1]

[Total 3 marks]

Exam Practice Tip

Knowing how the hormones that control the menstrual cycle interact with each other can be handy when it comes to
understanding how these hormones are used to control fertility. So make sure you've got it all sorted out in your head.

Topic B5 — Homeostasis and Response

More on Controlling Fertility

1 A couple want to have children but the woman has not yet become pregnant. Blood tests have shown that she has a low level of follicle stimulating hormone (FSH). She is treated with a fertility drug.

Grade 6-7

1.1 Explain why a low level of FSH may be preventing the woman from becoming pregnant.

....

[1]

1.2 In addition to FSH, which other hormone will the fertility drug contain to help the woman become pregnant? Give a reason for your answer.

....

....

[2]

1.3 Suggest **one** advantage and **one** disadvantage of this method of fertility treatment.

Advantage: ....

Disadvantage: ....

[2]

[Total 5 marks]

2 *In vitro* fertilisation is a reproductive treatment that can help people with fertility problems have children.

Grade 7-9

2.1 Describe the stages involved in a course of *in vitro* fertilisation treatment.

....

....

....

....

....

....

....

....

[5]

2.2 Give **two** disadvantages of *in vitro* fertilisation treatment.

....

....

....

[2]

[Total 7 marks]

Adrenaline and Thyroxine

The graph below shows the change in the level of a hormone controlled by a negative feedback response over time.
Use the words on the right to fill in the labels on the graph.

normal   low   stimulated

inhibited   high

.... level of hormone detected

release of hormone ....

.... level of hormone

.... level of hormone detected

release of hormone ....

Blood hormone level

Time

---

1 Thyroxine is a hormone.   *Grade 4-6*

1.1 Which statement best describes the role of thyroxine in the body? Tick **one** box.

☐ Thyroxine inhibits development.

☐ Thyroxine regulates basal metabolic rate.

☐ Thyroxine decreases heart rate.

[1]

1.2 Which gland produces thyroxine?

....

[1]

[Total 2 marks]

2 The hormone adrenaline is produced in times of fear or stress.   *Grade 6-7*

2.1 Where is adrenaline released from?

....

[1]

2.2 Describe the effect that adrenaline has on the body.

....

....

....

[3]

2.3 Name the response that adrenaline prepares the body for.

....

[1]

[Total 5 marks]

Topic B5 — Homeostasis and Response

DNA

1   DNA makes up the genetic material in animal and plant cells.   (Grade 4-6)

1.1   Which of the following statements about DNA is correct?
Tick **one** box.

☐   DNA is located in the cytoplasm of animal and plant cells.

☐   DNA is located in the ribosomes in animal and plant cells.

☐   DNA is located in the nucleus of animal and plant cells.

☐   DNA is located in vacuoles in animal and plant cells.

[1]

1.2   What are chromosomes?
Tick **one** box.

☐   Proteins coded for by DNA.

☐   The structures that contain DNA.

☐   The site of protein synthesis.

☐   The bases that make up DNA.

[1]

[Total 2 marks]

2   An organism's DNA contains lots of sections called genes.   (Grade 6-7)

2.1   Outline the function of genes.

....

....

[2]

2.2   What is meant by the term 'genome'?

....

....

[1]

2.3   Give **one** reason why it is important for scientists to have an understanding of the human genome.
Explain your answer.

....

....

....

....

....

[2]

[Total 5 marks]

 ☐   ☐   ☐

Reproduction

1 Reproduction can be sexual or asexual. Grade 4-6

In sexual reproduction, gametes from a male and female fuse together.

1.1 Name the male gamete in animals.

....

[1]

1.2 Name the female gamete in plants.

....

[1]

1.3 Which type of cell division is involved in the production of gametes?

....

[1]

Asexual reproduction does not involve gametes.

1.4 What name can be given to the cells resulting from asexual reproduction?

☐ gametes   ☐ clones   ☐ eggs   ☐ chromosomes

[1]

1.5 Name the type of cell division used in asexual reproduction.

....

[1]

[Total 5 marks]

2 Sexual reproduction involves the fusion of gametes to form a fertilised egg cell. Grade 6-7

2.1 Explain how a fertilised egg cell has the correct number of chromosomes.

....

....

....

[2]

2.2 Asexual and sexual reproduction are very different methods.
Give **four** ways in which asexual reproduction is different to sexual reproduction.

....

....

....

....

....

[4]

[Total 6 marks]

Meiosis

1   Sexual reproduction in humans involves meiosis. **Grade 4-6**

1.1   Where in the body does meiosis take place?

....
[1]

1.2   What happens to the DNA at the very start of meiosis, before the cell starts to divide?

....
[1]

1.3   How many cell divisions are there during the process of meiosis?

....
[1]

1.4   Briefly describe the results of meiosis.

....

....

....

....
[3]

[Total 6 marks]

2   During fertilisation, two gametes formed by meiosis join together. **Grade 4-6**

2.1   How many copies of each chromosome does the resulting cell have?

....
[1]

After the two gametes join to produce a fertilised egg, the cells divide repeatedly.

2.2   What type of cell division do these cells undergo?

....
[1]

2.3   The dividing cells form an embryo.
      What happens to the cells in the embryo as it develops in order to form the whole organism?

....

....
[1]

[Total 3 marks]

Exam Practice Tip

It's outrageously easy to get mixed up between meiosis and mitosis when the pressure is on in an exam. Remember, m<u>e</u>iosis is the one that makes — <u>e</u>ggs and sp<u>e</u>rm. Mi<u>t</u>osis makes <u>t</u>win (identical) cells. Even if you know the difference, it's still really easy to accidentally write one when you mean the other 'cos the words are so similar, so always check twice.

Topic B6 — Inheritance, Variation and Evolution

X and Y Chromosomes

1 In humans, the gender of offspring is determined by a pair of sex chromosomes — X and Y.

1.1 Including the sex chromosomes, how many chromosomes are there in a normal body cell?
Tick **one** box.

☐ 22 single chromosomes   ☐ 22 pairs of chromosomes

☐ 23 pairs of chromosomes   ☐ 23 single chromosomes

[1]

Figure 1 shows how the gender of offspring is determined.

Figure 1

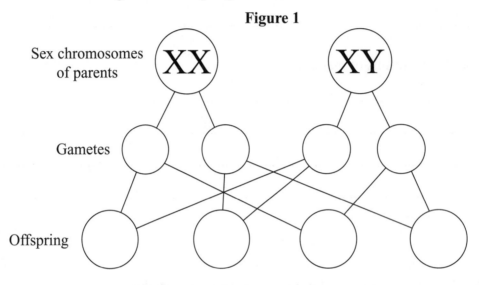

1.2 Circle the male parent in **Figure 1**.

[1]

1.3 Fill in the sex chromosomes of the gametes produced by each parent in **Figure 1**.

[1]

1.4 Complete **Figure 1** to show the combination of sex chromosomes in the offspring.

[1]

1.5 What is the ratio of male to female offspring?

....

[1]

1.6 Sex determination can also be shown in a Punnett square.
Produce a Punnett square to show how the gender of offspring is determined.

[2]

[Total 7 marks]

Topic B6 — Inheritance, Variation and Evolution

Genetic Diagrams

Use the words and phrases to complete the passage below. You don't have to use every one.

homozygous   dominant   multiple genes   genotypes   homologous
alleles   recessive   heterozygous   a single gene

Genes exist in different versions called .... These can be

dominant or .... If an individual has two copies of the same version

of a gene, they are said to be ...., but if they have two different

versions, they are said to be .... Some characteristics are controlled

by ...., but most are controlled by ....

1   **Figure 1** shows a family tree for the inheritance of a genetic disease.

Figure 1

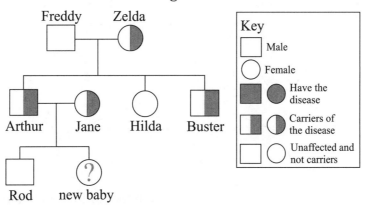

1.1 How can you tell that the allele for the disease is not dominant?

    ....

    ....

    [1]

1.2 The alleles for the disease are D and d. Both Arthur and Jane are carriers of the disease.
     Complete the Punnett square in **Figure 2** to determine the probability of their new baby
     being unaffected and not a carrier of the disease.

Figure 2

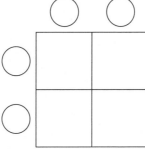

    probability = ... %

    [4]

    [Total 5 marks]

Topic B6 — Inheritance, Variation and Evolution

2   Hair length in dogs is controlled by two alleles. Short hair is caused by the dominant allele 'H' and long hair is caused by the recessive allele 'h'. **Figure 3** shows a genetic diagram of a cross between two dogs with the genotype Hh.

Figure 3

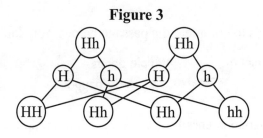

2.1 What is the expected ratio of long-haired puppies to short-haired puppies in this cross?

....
                                                                                                                                          [1]

2.2 A dog with the genotype HH was crossed with a dog with the genotype hh.
     They had 8 puppies. How many of those puppies would you expect to have long fur?

     Complete **Figure 4** below to explain your answer.

Figure 4

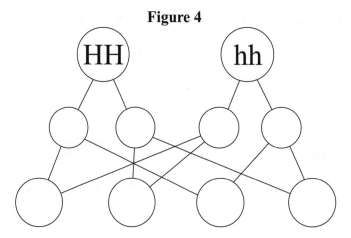

                                        number of long-haired puppies = ...
                                                                                                     [3]

2.3 A male dog heterozygous for short hair was then crossed with a female dog homozygous for long hair. What would you expect the ratio of long-haired to short-haired puppies to be in the offspring of this cross?

     Construct a Punnett square to explain your answer.

                                                                               ratio = ...
                                                                                                     [3]

                                                                                        [Total 7 marks]

Topic B6 — Inheritance, Variation and Evolution

Inherited Disorders

1 Polydactyly and cystic fibrosis are examples of inherited disorders. *(Grade 6-7)*

1.1 What are the symptoms of polydactyly?

....

[1]

1.2 A person only has to have one allele for polydactyly to have symptoms.
What does this tell you about the allele that causes polydactyly?

....

[1]

1.3 Even if both parents each carry one copy of the allele that causes cystic fibrosis, there is only
a relatively small chance that their offspring will have the disorder. Explain why this is the case.

....

....

....

[3]

[Total 5 marks]

2 Embryos can be screened for genetic disorders like cystic fibrosis.
The results of screening sometimes results in the embryo being destroyed.
There are lots of arguments for and against embryo screening. *(Grade 7-9)*

2.1 Suggest **three** arguments against embryo screening.

....

....

....

....

....

....

[3]

2.2 Suggest **three** arguments for embryo screening.

....

....

....

....

....

....

[3]

[Total 6 marks]

Topic B6 — Inheritance, Variation and Evolution

Variation

1   Variation occurs in many different organisms.

1.1   Dalmations and pugs are both members of the same species. However, they look
very different. For example, dalmations have spots but pugs do not.
What type of variation is causing this difference?

....

[1]

Figure 1 and **Figure 2** show two plants of the same species growing in opposite corners of a
garden. The plant in **Figure 1** was grown in a sunny corner, whereas the plant in **Figure 2** was
grown in a shady corner.

1.2   What type of variation is causing the differences between the two plants?

....

[1]

[Total 2 marks]

2   Mutations can occasionally lead to a rapid change in a species.
Explain how a mutation could lead to a rapid change in a species.

....

....

....

....

[Total 3 marks]

Exam Practice Tip

Remember that while variation can be caused by either genetic or environmental factors, it's usually caused by a mixture
of both interacting with each other. In the exam, you might get an example of variation that you've never heard of before.
Don't worry if you do, all the information you need to answer the question will be there. Just apply your knowledge.

Topic B6 — Inheritance, Variation and Evolution

Evolution

1 Extinction is when a species completely dies out because they're not able to evolve quickly enough to adapt to a change in their environment. Give **five** factors that can cause a species to become extinct.

Grade
6-7

....

....

....

....

....

[Total 5 marks]

2 **Figure 1** and **Figure 2** show two hares. The hare in **Figure 1** lives in a very cold climate. The hare in **Figure 2** lives in a warmer climate.

Grade
7-9

Figure 1　　　　**Figure 2**

The hare in **Figure 2** uses its large ears as a cooling mechanism. They allow lots of heat to leave the hare's body. The hare in **Figure 1** has smaller ears.

Suggest how the species of hare in **Figure 1** evolved to have smaller ears than hares that live in warmer climates.

....

....

....

....

....

....

....

....

....

[Total 5 marks]

Selective Breeding

1 Selective breeding is used in several different industries. (Grade 4-6)

1.1 Which of these is another name for the process of selective breeding?
Tick **one** box.

☐ Evolution   ☐ Natural selection   ☐ Inheritance   ☐ Artificial selection

[1]

1.2 What is selective breeding?

....

....

[1]

1.3 Suggest why dairy farmers might use selective breeding.

....

[1]

[Total 3 marks]

2 A dog breeder used selective breeding to produce a litter of puppies that all had a good, gentle temperament. (Grade 6-7)

2.1* Describe how the breeder could have achieved this, starting from a mixed population of dogs.

....

....

....

....

....

....

[4]

2.2 Suggest why the puppies may be more susceptible to genetic defects.

....

....

....

[2]

2.3 Suggest why a new disease might be an issue for the puppies produced using selective breeding.

....

....

....

[3]

[Total 9 marks]

Topic B6 — Inheritance, Variation and Evolution

Genetic Engineering

Draw circles to show whether the statements below are **true** or **false**.

Genetic engineering can only be carried out on plants. True / False

Genetic engineering has been proven to be 100% risk free. True / False

Crops that have been genetically engineered are already being grown. True / False

Vectors in genetic engineering can be bacterial plasmids. True / False

1 Genetic engineering is being investigated for use in a wide variety of applications. Grade 6-7

1.1 What is genetic engineering?

....

....

[2]

The process of genetic engineering has several steps.

1.2 The useful gene is first isolated from an organism's DNA.
Explain how this is done.

....

....

[1]

1.3 The gene is then inserted into the target organism's genome.
Explain how this is achieved so that the organism develops with the desired characteristics.

....

....

....

....

[3]

1.4 Scientists are currently investigating the applications of genetic engineering in medicine.
Give **two** examples of how genetic engineering has been used to treat human diseases,
or how it could potentially be used.

....

....

....

....

[2]

[Total 8 marks]

2 Genetic engineering can be used to alter the genes and characteristics of food crops. The resulting crops are known as GM crops.

Grade 6-7

2.1 What does 'GM' stand for when referring to crops that have been genetically engineered?
Tick **one** box.

☐ genetically manufactured ☐ genetically mutated ☐ genetically modelled ☐ genetically modified

[1]

2.2 GM crops are often altered to increase their yield. One way in which this can be achieved in some crops is by modifying their genes to make them produce larger fruit.
Suggest **two** other ways in which a crop plant's genes can be altered to increase its yield.

....

....

[2]

A scientist was researching the effect of a genetic modification on fruit size in a species of plant.
He first grew a normal individual of the species in controlled conditions (Plant 1).
He then measured the circumferences of the 10 largest fruits after a set amount of time.
He repeated these steps with a genetically modified individual from the same species (Plant 2).
Table 1 shows the results.

Table 1

	Fruit Circumference (cm)									
Plant 1	16.4	16.8	15.9	16.2	15.7	16.4	16.3	16.0	15.9	16.0
Plant 2	20.2	20.4	19.8	19.6	20.4	20.6	20.2	19.9	20.1	20.0

2.3 Use the data in **Table 1** to calculate the mean fruit circumference for each plant.

Plant 1 = ... cm   Plant 2 = ... cm
[2]

2.4 Calculate the percentage change in mean fruit circumference between Plant 1 and Plant 2.

.............%
[2]

2.5 Not everyone thinks that GM crops are a good idea.
Give **one** concern that people may have about GM crops.

....

....

[1]

[Total 8 marks]

Fossils

1   The fossil record provides an account of how much different organisms have changed over time. Fossils can be formed in three ways.

1.1 **Figure 1** shows a fossilised insect preserved in amber. Amber is fossilised tree sap. The insect became trapped in the sap as it fed from the tree.

Figure 1

Explain how insects trapped in amber become fossilised rather than decaying.

....

....

[2]

1.2 Describe **two** other ways that fossils are formed.

....

....

....

....

[2]

1.3 Scientists are unable to use the fossil record as conclusive evidence to support or disprove theories on how life on Earth first began. Explain why this is the case.

....

....

....

....

....

....

[3]

[Total 7 marks]

Antibiotic-Resistant Bacteria

1   Antibiotic resistance in bacteria is becoming an increasing problem in medicine. This is partly due to the overuse of antibiotics.   **Grade 4-6**

1.1   The overuse of antibiotics is sometimes caused by them being prescribed inappropriately. Give **two** examples of antibiotics being prescribed inappropriately.

....

....

[2]

1.2   Explain why patients prescribed a course of antibiotics should always complete the full course.

....

....

....

[3]

[Total 5 marks]

2   Antibiotic-resistant strains of bacteria are harder to treat because the conventional antibiotics used to kill them are now ineffective. New antibiotics are being developed, but it's unlikely that we'll be able to keep up with the emergence of new resistant strains.   **Grade 6-7**

2.1   Explain why the development of antibiotics is unlikely to keep up with the emergence of new antibiotic-resistant bacteria.

....

....

[2]

2.2   Explain how antibiotic-resistant strains of bacteria develop and spread.

....

....

....

....

....

....

....

....

[5]

[Total 7 marks]

Topic B6 — Inheritance, Variation and Evolution

Classification

1 Evolutionary trees show how scientists think that organisms are related to each other. **Figure 1** shows the evolutionary tree for species A – K.

Figure 1

1.1 Give **two** pieces of information that scientists use to prepare evolutionary trees for living and extinct organisms.

....

[2]

1.2 Which species is the most recent common ancestor of species G and species J?

....

[1]

1.3 Which pair of species, G and H or J and K are more distantly related?

....

[1]

[Total 4 marks]

2 Organisms used to be classified into groups using the Linnaean system.

2.1 What is the correct order for the groups of the Linnaean system, from largest to smallest?
Tick **one** box.

☐ kingdom, phylum, class, order, family, genus, species

☐ species, genus, class, phylum, order, family, kingdom

☐ kingdom, family, phylum, order, class, genus, species

☐ species, class, genus, family, order, phylum, kingdom

[1]

A new classification system, known as the three-domain system, was proposed in the 1990s. In this system, organisms are first divided into domains.

2.2 What is the name of the scientist who proposed the three-domain system?

....

[1]

2.3 Which of the domains includes primitive bacteria often found in extreme environments?

....

[1]

2.4 Other than fungi, state **three** types of organisms found in the domain Eukaryota.

....

[3]

[Total 6 marks]

Topic B6 — Inheritance, Variation and Evolution

Competition

1   The plants in a community are often in competition with each other for water and mineral ions.   *Grade 4-6*

1.1   Where do plants obtain water and mineral ions from?

....

[1]

1.2   Name **two** other factors that plants often compete with each other for.

....

....

[2]

1.3   The animals in a community also compete with each other.
State **three** factors animals compete with each other for.

....

....

....

[3]

[Total 6 marks]

2   Within a community, each species depends on other species for things such as food, shelter, pollination and seed dispersal.   *Grade 6-7*

2.1   What is this type of relationship called?

....

[1]

Blue tits are relatively common birds that live in woodland communities.
Blue tits feed on caterpillars. Caterpillars live and feed on plants.

2.2   If the caterpillars were removed from the community, suggest what might happen to the numbers of blue tits and plants. Explain your answers.

....

....

....

....

[4]

2.3   Some communities are not stable.
Explain fully what is meant by the term 'stable community'.

....

....

[2]

[Total 7 marks]

Abiotic and Biotic Factors

1 In an ecosystem, there will be both biotic and abiotic factors. **(Grade 4-6)**

1.1 Which of the following statements is correct? Tick **one** box.

☐ Light intensity, temperature and carbon dioxide level are all examples of biotic factors.

☐ Availability of food, carbon dioxide level and pathogens are all examples of abiotic factors.

☐ Light intensity, temperature and carbon dioxide level are all examples of abiotic factors.

☐ Availability of food, light intensity and pathogens are all examples of biotic factors.

[1]

1.2 Suggest **one** abiotic factor that could affect the distribution of animals living in aquatic areas.

....

[1]

1.3 Suggest **two** abiotic factors that could affect the distribution of plants growing in soil.

....

....

[2]

[Total 4 marks]

2 Red squirrels are native to southern Britain. When grey squirrels were introduced into the same area, the number of red squirrels declined. **(Grade 6-7)**

Suggest why the number of red squirrels declined.

....

....

....

[Total 3 marks]

3 Grasses make their own food by photosynthesis. In grassland communities, the grass leaves provide insects with shelter, a place to breed and a source of food. Visiting birds feed on insects. **(Grade 6-7)**

The birds that visit the grassland to feed become infected with a new pathogen that eventually kills them. What would you expect to happen to the number of grass plants? Explain your answer.

....

....

....

....

[Total 3 marks]

Topic B7 — Ecology

Adaptations

1 Some organisms live in environments that are very extreme, such as environments with a high salt concentration.

Grade 4-6

1.1 What name is given to organisms that live in extreme environments?

....

[1]

1.2 Name **one** group of organisms that can live in deep sea vents where temperatures are very high.

....

[1]

1.3 Describe **one** extreme condition, other than a high salt concentration or a high temperature, that some organisms can tolerate.

....

[1]

[Total 3 marks]

2 Organisms are adapted to the conditions in which they live. **Figure 1** shows a camel and **Figure 2** shows a cactus. Both camels and cacti live in hot, dry desert conditions.

Grade 6-7

Figure 1

long eyelashes

large feet

Figure 2

spines

swollen stem

2.1 Suggest how each of the features in **Figure 1** allow the camel to live in desert conditions.

Long eyelashes ....

....

Large feet...

....

[2]

2.2 Suggest how having spines instead of leaves allows cacti to live in desert conditions.

....

[1]

2.3 Suggest how having a swollen storage stem allows cacti to live in desert conditions.

....

[1]

Cacti can have two types of roots — shallow, wide-spreading roots or long, deep roots.

2.4 For each of these types of root, suggest how the cacti are better adapted to live in desert conditions.

....

....

[2]

[Total 6 marks]

3 Lizards gain most of their heat from the environment. This means that their body temperatures change with the temperature of the environment. **Figure 3** shows a lizard.

Grade 6-7

Figure 3

Lizards control their body temperatures by adapting their behaviour to changes in the environment. For example, in the early morning they lie in the sun to gain heat and only then can they become active.

3.1 Suggest what behavioural adaptation lizards might show when the environmental temperature becomes too hot.

....

[1]

Some lizards also have a structural adaptation that helps them to control their body temperature. They can change the colour of their skin within a range from light to dark. Darker colours absorb more heat than lighter colours.

3.2 Would you expect a lizard in cold conditions to have a dark or light coloured skin?

....

[1]

3.3 There are different types of adaptation, including behavioural and structural. Name **one** other type of adaptation that organisms can have.

....

[1]

[Total 3 marks]

Exam Practice Tip

All of the organisms on these pages are different and have different adaptations to their environment. You could be given information on any organism in the exam but, remember, each feature that the organism has gives it an advantage for living in its environment. You just need to have a think about what that advantage could be. Simple.

Topic B7 — Ecology

Food Chains

On the food chain below, label the producer and the secondary consumer.

seaweed ⟶ fish ⟶ shark ⟶ whale

1   **Figure 1** shows an example of a woodland food chain.

Figure 1

green plants ⟶ greenflies ⟶ blue tits ⟶ sparrow hawk

1.1 What term would be used to describe the greenflies' position in **Figure 1**?

....

[1]

1.2 Green plants produce biomass for the rest of the food chain. Explain how they do this.

....

....

[3]

[Total 4 marks]

2   In a stable community, the numbers of predators and prey rise and fall in cycles as shown in **Figure 2**. In this cycle the predator is a lynx and the prey is a snowshoe hare.

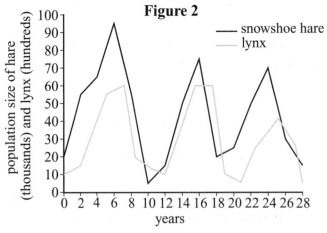

2.1 Describe and explain what happens to the number of lynx between years 4 and 6.

....

....

[2]

2.2 What causes the number of snowshoe hares to fall between years 6 and 10?

....

[1]

[Total 3 marks]

Using Quadrats

1   A group of students used a quadrat with an area of 0.5 m² to investigate the number of buttercups growing in a field. They counted the number of buttercups in the quadrat in ten randomly selected places. **Table 1** shows their results.

Table 1

Quadrat Number	Number of buttercups
1	15
2	13
3	16
4	23
5	26
6	23
7	13
8	12
9	16
10	13

1.1 Why is it important that the quadrats were placed randomly in the field?

....
                                                                                                                [1]

1.2 What is the modal number of buttercups in **Table 1**?

.... buttercups
                                                                                                                [1]

1.3 What is the median number of buttercups in **Table 1**?

.... buttercups
                                                                                                                [1]

1.4 Calculate the mean number of buttercups per 0.5 m² quadrat.

.... buttercups per 0.5 m²
                                                                                                                [1]

1.5 The total area of the field was 1750 m².
     Estimate the number of buttercups in the whole of the field.

.... buttercups
                                                                                                                [3]

                                                                                        [Total 7 marks]

Topic B7 — Ecology

Using Transects

1   A transect was carried out from the edge of a small pond, across a grassy field and into a woodland. The distributions of four species of plant were recorded along the transect, along with the soil moisture and light levels. **Figure 1** shows the results.

Figure 1

Key dandelion   short grass   long grass
     daisy

pond   zone A   zone B   zone C   woodland

soil moisture level: high ⟶ low
light level: high ⟶ low

The grassy field is split up into three zones — A, B and C.

1.1 In **Figure 1**, which zones contained only one species of plant?

....
                                                                                                                      [1]

1.2 Which of the four species of plant can grow in soils with both a high and low moisture level, and at both low and high light intensities?

....
                                                                                                                      [1]

1.3 Suggest **two** reasons why long grass, daisies and dandelions all grow in zone A.

....

....
                                                                                                                      [2]

Children often play football on one zone of the grassy field.
The trampling that occurs here makes it difficult for plants to become established.

1.4 Suggest which zone might be used to play football. Explain your answer.

....

....
                                                                                                                      [2]

1.5 Suggest why there are no daisies or dandelions growing in the woodland.

....
                                                                                                                      [1]

A transect can also be used to determine the abundance of species in an ecosystem.

1.6 Explain how this transect could be used to determine the abundance of the four plant species.

....
                                                                                                                      [1]

[Total 8 marks]

The Water Cycle

Warm-Up

Warm-Up

Choose from the words below to complete the sentences about the water cycle. Some words may not be used at all.

precipitation   evaporate   warms   cools   water vapour   carbon dioxide   condense

Energy from the Sun makes water .... from the land and sea,

turning it into .... This is carried upwards. When it gets higher

up it .... and condenses to form clouds. Water falls from the

clouds as .... onto land. It then drains into the sea, before the

whole process starts again.

1   **Figure 1** represents the stages in the water cycle.   Grade 4-6

Figure 1

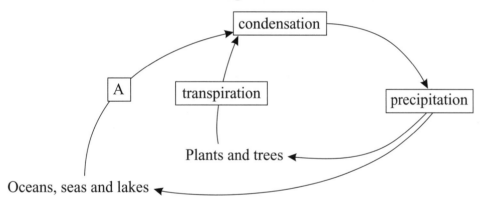

1.1 Name the process represented by **A** in the diagram.

....

[1]

1.2 Outline what is meant by the term 'precipitation'.

....

[1]

1.3 Explain why precipitation is an important stage in the water cycle.

....

....

[1]

[3 marks]

Topic B7 — Ecology

The Carbon Cycle

1   **Figure 1** shows an unfinished diagram of the carbon cycle.

Figure 1

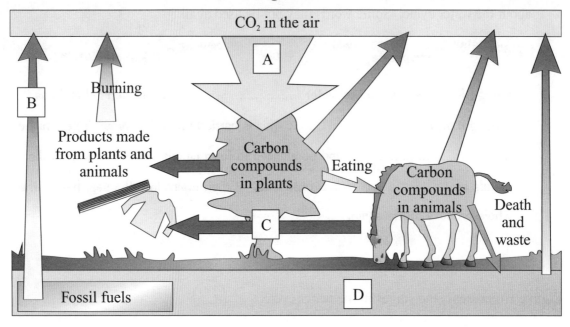

1.1 Name the process represented by **A** in **Figure 1**.

....

[1]

1.2 Which group of organisms remove carbon dioxide from the air?

....

[1]

1.3 Name the process represented by **B** in **Figure 1**.

....

[1]

1.4 Box **C** is the process of changing animal components into products. These can be recycled
     to return carbon dioxide to the air. Suggest **one** animal product that can be recycled in this way.

....

[1]

1.5 Process **D** in **Figure 1** is decay. Describe the importance of decay in the carbon cycle.

....

....

[2]

[Total 6 marks]

Exam Practice Tip

In the exam you could be tested on any part of the carbon cycle, so make sure you know the whole of it and not just bits
of it. Try sketching the whole cycle out and make sure you can link each bit together. Don't have your arrows going the
wrong way round, and make sure you understand why the carbon is moving around, e.g. because of respiration. Sorted.

Biodiversity and Waste Management

1 Many human activities have an impact on biodiversity. Grade 4-6

1.1 Define biodiversity.

....

....

[1]

1.2 Suggest **one** human activity that reduces biodiversity.

....

[1]

[Total 2 marks]

2 The global population is using an increasing amount of resources. Grade 4-6

2.1 State **two** reasons why humans are using more resources.

....

....

[2]

If waste is not handled correctly, pollution levels in water and in the air will increase.

2.2 State **two** ways that water can become polluted.

....

....

[2]

2.3 State **two** substances that pollute the air when they are released into the atmosphere.

....

[2]

[Total 6 marks]

3 Herbicides are used by farmers to control the growth of weeds on land where crops are grown. Grade 6-7

3.1 Give **two** reasons why using a herbicide can reduce biodiversity.

....

....

[2]

3.2 Explain why a high biodiversity creates a stable ecosystem.

....

....

....

[2]

[Total 4 marks]

Topic B7 — Ecology

Global Warming

Fill in the gaps in the passage below using the words on the right.
Not all words need to be used, but each word can only be used once.

insulating

the Sun

reflect

increases

the moon   space

gases   decreases

volcanoes

The temperature of the Earth is a balance between the energy

it gets from .... and the energy it radiates

back into .... The .... in the

atmosphere act like an insulating layer. They radiate some of

the energy back towards the Earth. This ....

the temperature of the planet.

---

1   Global warming is caused by the increasing
     levels of 'greenhouse gases' in the atmosphere.   Grade 6-7

1.1   Which of the following pairs of gases are the main contributors to global warming?
      Tick **one** box.

      ☐ carbon dioxide and sulfur dioxide

      ☐ carbon dioxide and methane

      ☐ sulfur dioxide and nitrogen dioxide

      ☐ nitrogen dioxide and methane

                                                                                    [1]

      There are a number of consequences of global warming,
      including land becoming flooded.

1.2   Suggest why global warming might cause land to become flooded.

      ....

      ....
                                                                                    [2]

1.3   Suggest **two** other consequences of global warming.

      ....

      ....
                                                                                    [2]
                                                                        [Total 5 marks]

Exam Practice Tip

Greenhouse gases cause the 'greenhouse effect', but don't go getting this muddled up with global warming. Without these
gases trapping energy in Earth's atmosphere, it'd be too cold for us to survive. But the increasing amounts of these gases
are increasing the amount of energy being trapped, and that's why we're getting all, ahem, hot and bothered about them.

Topic B7 — Ecology

Deforestation and Land Use

1 State **two** ways in which humans reduce the amount of land available for other animals and plants.

Grade 4-6

....

....

[Total 2 marks]

2 Peat bogs are sometimes destroyed so that the peat can be burnt as fuel.

Grade 6-7

2.1 Give **one** other reason why peat bogs are destroyed by humans.

....

[1]

2.2 Explain what problem burning peat can cause.

....

....

[2]

2.3 Explain the effect that the destruction of peat bogs has on biodiversity.

....

....

[2]

[Total 5 marks]

3 Biofuel production has caused large-scale deforestation.

Grade 6-7

3.1 Explain why large-scale deforestation has been required to produce biofuels.

....

[1]

3.2 State **two** other reasons for large-scale deforestation.

....

....

[2]

[Total 3 marks]

4 Suggest and explain **two** harmful effects on the environment caused by the destruction of large areas of trees.

Grade 7-9

....

....

....

....

[Total 4 marks]

Maintaining Ecosystems and Biodiversity

1 In some areas, programmes have been put in place to reduce the negative effects of human activity on ecosystems and biodiversity.

Grade 4-6

1.1 Which of the following would reduce carbon dioxide emissions into the atmosphere? Tick **one** box.

☐ Setting up more breeding programmes for endangered species.

☐ Cutting down large areas of trees for housing development.

☐ Increasing the number of power stations.

☐ Burning fewer fossil fuels.

[1]

1.2 The government encourages people to recycle as much of their waste as possible.
Suggest how this could help to protect ecosystems.

....

....

[2]

[Total 3 marks]

2 Monoculture is a form of agriculture in which only one type of crop is grown in a field.

Grade 6-7

2.1 Suggest what effect monoculture has on biodiversity. Explain your answer.

....

....

[2]

2.2 Explain why farmers who grow crops using monoculture may be advised
to leave strips of grassland and plant hedgerows around the edges of their crops.

....

[1]

[Total 3 marks]

3 Suggest why some people might be opposed to programmes that maintain biodiversity.

Grade 7-9

....

....

....

....

....

....

....

[Total 4 marks]

Atoms

Choose from the labels below to fill in the blanks in the passage.

protons

1×10^{-14}

0.1

1/10 000

charge   electrons

The radius of an atom is approximately .... nanometres.

The radius of the nucleus is around .... metres.

That's about .... of the radius of an atom.

An atom doesn't have an overall .... as it has equal

numbers of .... and ....

1   **Figure 1** shows the structure of a helium atom.   (Grade 4-6)

Figure 1

1.1 Name the region where most of the mass of the atom is concentrated.

....

[1]

1.2 What is the relative charge of particle **B**?

....

[1]

1.3 Name the particles in region **A** and give their relative charges.

....

....

[2]

[Total 4 marks]

2   A potassium atom can be represented by the nuclear symbol $^{39}_{19}K$.   (Grade 4-6)

2.1 What is the mass number of $^{39}_{19}K$?

....

[1]

2.2 What is the atomic number of $^{39}_{19}K$?

....

[1]

2.3 How many protons, neutrons and electrons does an atom of $^{39}_{19}K$ have?

protons: ....   neutrons: ....   electrons: ....

[3]

[Total 5 marks]

Elements

1 $^{35}_{17}Cl$ and $^{37}_{17}Cl$ are the naturally occurring isotopes of the element chlorine. Grade 4-6

1.1 Which of the following statements about elements is true? Tick **one** box.

Atoms of an element can contain different numbers of protons. ☐

Chlorine is one of 200 different elements. ☐

Elements contain more than one type of atom. ☐

Atoms are the smallest part of an element that can exist. ☐

[1]

1.2 Explain why $^{35}_{17}Cl$ and $^{37}_{17}Cl$ are isotopes of the element chlorine.

....

....

....

[2]

[Total 3 marks]

2 This question is about isotopes. Grade 6-7

2.1 A neutral atom of sulfur, ^{32}S, has 16 electrons.
Sulfur has three other naturally occurring isotopes, with mass numbers 33, 34 and 36.
Complete the table below giving the number of protons, neutrons and electrons for each isotope.

isotope	number of protons	number of neutrons	number of electrons	% abundance
^{32}S	....	....	16	94.99
^{33}S	....	....	....	0.75
^{34}S	....	....	....	4.25
^{36}S	....	....	....	0.01

[3]

2.2 Using the information in the table above, calculate the relative atomic mass of sulfur.
Give your answer to one decimal place.

Relative atomic mass: ....

[2]

2.3 Atom **X** has a mass number of 51 and an atomic number of 23.
Atom **Y** has a mass number of 51 and an atomic number of 22.
Atom **Z** has a mass number of 52 and an atomic number of 23.

Identify which of the atoms are isotopes and explain why.

....

....

[3]

[Total 8 marks]

Topic C1 — Atomic Structure and the Periodic Table

Compounds

1 Ammonia is a compound with the formula NH$_3$. (Grade 4-6)

1.1 Why is ammonia classified as a compound? Tick **one** box.

It contains only one type of atom. ☐

It contains two elements chemically combined. ☐

It cannot be broken down into elements using chemical methods. ☐

It contains more than one atom. ☐

[1]

1.2 How many atoms are there in a single molecule of ammonia?

....

[1]

[Total 2 marks]

2 The following list contains a variety of substances identified by their chemical formula. (Grade 6-7)

A. O$_2$ **B.** NaCl   **C.** C$_2$H$_4$ **D.** P$_4$ **E.** H$_2$O   **F.** H$_2$

2.1 Name substance **B**.

....

[1]

2.2 Identify **one** substance from the list that is a compound. Explain your choice.

....

....

[2]

2.3 How many atoms are there in a molecule of substance **C**?

....

[1]

2.4 **C** and **F** were reacted to form C$_2$H$_6$. Using the formulas of the substances, state if a new compound has been made and explain your answer.

....

....

....

[1]

[Total 5 marks]

Exam Practice Tip

Make sure you know the difference between atoms, elements and compounds. Here's a quick summary... Everything is made of atoms (which contain protons, neutrons and electrons). Elements only contain one type of atom (all the atoms have the same number of protons). A compound consists of different atoms joined together by chemical bonds. Got it?

 ☐   ☐   ☐

Topic C1 — Atomic Structure and the Periodic Table

Chemical Equations

The chemical word equation for a reaction is shown below:

magnesium + hydrochloric acid → magnesium chloride + hydrogen

For each of the following statements circle whether the statement is **true** or **false**.

1) Hydrogen is a product in the reaction   True   Or   False

2) The equation shows the reaction between chlorine and hydrogen   True   Or   False

3) Hydrochloric acid is a reactant   True   Or   False

4) The equation shows the reaction between magnesium and hydrochloric acid   True   Or   False

1   Sodium (Na) reacts vigorously with chlorine gas (Cl_2) to form sodium chloride (NaCl) only.

1.1   Write a word equation for this reaction.

....

[1]

1.2   Which of the following equations correctly represents this reaction?

$Na + Cl \rightarrow NaCl$ ☐

$Na_2 + 2Cl \rightarrow 2NaCl$ ☐

$Na_2 + Cl_2 \rightarrow 2NaCl$ ☐

$2Na + Cl_2 \rightarrow 2NaCl$ ☐

[1]

[Total 2 marks]

2   Nitric acid can be made using ammonia.

2.1   The first stage in the manufacture of nitric acid is to oxidise ammonia, NH_3, to nitrogen(II) oxide, NO. Balance the equation for the reaction.

.... NH_3 + ... O_2 → .... NO + ... H_2O

[1]

2.2   The reaction below shows the final stage in the manufacture of nitric acid. The equation is not balanced correctly. Explain how you can tell.

$$2NO_2 + O_2 + H_2O \rightarrow 2HNO_3$$

....

....

[1]

[Total 2 marks]

Topic C1 — Atomic Structure and the Periodic Table

Mixtures and Chromatography

1 Air contains many gases. It mainly consists of nitrogen, N_2, and oxygen, O_2 with a small amount of carbon dioxide, CO_2. There are also trace amounts of noble gases such as argon, Ar.

Grade 4-6

1.1 Is air an element, compound or mixture? Explain your answer.

....

....

....

[3]

1.2 Argon can be separated out from air. Will the chemical properties of argon as a separate gas be different from the properties of argon in air? Explain your answer.

....

....

[2]

[Total 5 marks]

2* A simple chromatography experiment was set up to separate dyes in inks. Samples of three different water soluble inks, A, B and C, were placed on a piece of chromatography paper. After 30 minutes, the chromatogram in **Figure 1** was obtained.

Grade 6-7

Figure 1

PRACTICAL

Solvent front

Solvent origin

A B C

Outline the procedure for setting up and running this experiment and explain the results.

....

....

....

....

....

....

....

....

[Total 6 marks]

Topic C1 — Atomic Structure and the Periodic Table

More Separation Techniques

1 A student was given a mixture of insoluble chalk powder and solid potassium chloride. Potassium chloride is water soluble. *Grade 6-7*

1.1 Outline a method for separating the chalk from potassium chloride.

....

....

....

[3]

1.2 Outline the process the student could use to obtain pure crystals of potassium chloride from a potassium chloride solution.

....

....

....

[1]

[Total 4 marks]

2 Powdered iron and powdered sulfur were mixed together. Information on the solubility of iron and sulfur is given in **Table 1**. *Grade 7-9*

Table 1

	Iron	Sulfur
Solubility in water	Insoluble	Insoluble
Solubility in methylbenzene	Insoluble	Soluble

2.1 Using the information in **Table 1**, explain how the iron and sulfur could be separated out again to form pure iron and crystals of sulfur.

....

....

....

....

....

[3]

2.2 Some of the mixture was heated in a fume cupboard. Iron(II) sulfide formed. A student stated the iron and sulfur could be separated back out using physical processes. Is the student correct? Explain your answer.

....

....

....

[3]

[Total 6 marks]

Topic C1 — Atomic Structure and the Periodic Table

Distillation

1 Sucrose is a sugar with the formula $C_{12}H_{22}O_{11}$. It is soluble in water. **Grade 4-6**

Which of the following techniques would be best for obtaining pure water from a sugar solution? Tick **one** box.

☐ Evaporation ☐ Condensation ☐ Simple distillation ☐ Fractional distillation

[Total 1 mark]

2 A solution containing octane, which has a boiling point of 125 °C, was prepared. The solution contained an impurity with a boiling point of 187 °C. The distillation apparatus shown in **Figure 1** was set up to separate the octane from the impurity. **Grade 6-7**

Figure 1

Distillation flask

Solution containing octane and soluble impurity

D

Heat

2.1 The apparatus is not correctly set up.
Explain how you would modify the apparatus to make it function correctly.

....

....

[1]

2.2 Explain how octane is separated from the impurity when the distillation apparatus is set up correctly. Include the function of D in your answer.

....

....

....

....

[3]

2.3 If the distillation flask was placed in a boiling water bath and not directly heated, the octane would not distill. Explain why.

....

....

[2]

[Total 6 marks]

 ☐   ☐ ☺ ☐

Topic C1 — Atomic Structure and the Periodic Table

The History of The Atom

For the following statements, circle whether they are **true** or **false**.

New experimental evidence can disprove models	True	Or	False
Scientific models can be based on existing theories and new experimental evidence	True	Or	False
Older scientific theories must be ignored when new ones are adopted	True	Or	False

1 Models of the atom have changed over time. (Grade 4-6)

1.1 Which of the following statements is the best description of what scientists thought an atom was like before the electron was discovered?
Tick **one** box.

☐ Tiny solid spheres that can't be divided. ☐ Formless 'clouds' of matter. ☐ Flat geometric shapes. ☐ Discrete packets of energy.

[1]

1.2 Draw one line from each atomic model to the correct description of that model.

Atomic Model

Plum pudding model

Bohr's model

Rutherford's nuclear model

Description

A positively charged 'ball' with negatively charged electrons in it.

A small positively charged nucleus surrounded by a 'cloud' of negative electrons.

Electrons in fixed orbits surrounding a small positively charged nucleus.

Solid spheres with a different sphere for each element.

[3]

1.3 In 1932, James Chadwick discovered a neutral sub-atomic particle found in the nucleus. Give the name of this particle.

....

[1]

[Total 5 marks]

2 In 1911, Ernest Rutherford fired alpha particles at gold foil. Most of the alpha particles passed straight through the gold foil without being deflected. Only a few of the particles bounced back at 180°.

Grade 6-7

2.1 Explain why most of the alpha particles passed through the foil.

....

....

[1]

2.2 Name the scientist that adapted Rutherford's nuclear model by suggesting that electrons orbit the nucleus at specific distances.

....

[1]

[Total 2 marks]

3 In 1897, J. J. Thomson discovered the electron. This discovery led Thomson to propose the 'plum pudding' model of the atom.

Grade 7-9

3.1 Thomson realised that there must be positive charge in an atom as well as the negative charge of the electrons. Suggest how Thomson could have worked this out using his knowledge of the atom and its charge.

....

....

[2]

3.2* Describe similarities and differences between the plum pudding model and the modern nuclear model of the atom.

....

....

....

....

....

....

....

....

....

....

[6]

[Total 8 marks]

Exam Practice Tip

When looking at the history of the atom, it's not only important that you know the different theories of atomic structure — you also need to understand why, and describe how, scientific theories develop over time. So make sure you go through your notes on Working Scientifically before the exam. And then why not relax with some plum pudding...

Topic C1 — Atomic Structure and the Periodic Table

Electronic Structure

1 Calcium is a reactive metal with an atomic number of 20. (Grade 4-6)

1.1 What is the electron configuration of a neutral calcium atom? Tick **one** box.

☐ 2, 18 ☐ 2, 16, 2 ☐ 2, 8, 8, 2 ☐ 2, 2, 8, 8

[1]

1.2 Calcium has two electrons in its innermost shell. Explain why.

....

....

[2]

[Total 3 marks]

2 Electronic structures can be represented in different ways. (Grade 6-7)

Figure 1

2.1 **Figure 1** shows the electronic structure of an atom of chlorine.
Give the electronic structure of chlorine in number form.

Chlorine: ....

[1]

2.2 Draw the electronic structure of sulfur.

[2]

2.3 **Figure 2** shows the electronic structure of an atom of an element, **X**. Identify element **X**.

Figure 2

Element **X**: ....

[1]

[Total 4 marks]

Exam Practice Tip

Electronic structures are the key to understanding lots of chemistry, so it's really important that you know how to work them out. Definitely make sure you know, or can work out, the electronic structures for the first 20 elements in the periodic table before going into your exam. It'll help you in all manner of questions, believe me.

Topic C1 — Atomic Structure and the Periodic Table ☹ ☐ ☺ ☐ ☺ ☐

Development of The Periodic Table

1 Mendeleev, guided by atomic masses, grouped elements with similar properties to form an early version of the periodic table. He used his table to predict properties of undiscovered elements such as eka-silicon, now called germanium. **Table 1** shows some predictions.

Table 1

	Silicon (Si)	**Eka-silicon (Ek)**	**Tin (Sn)**
Atomic Mass	28	72	119
Density in g/cm³	2.3	**D**	7.3
Appearance	grey/silver non-metal	grey metal	grey metal
Formula of oxide	SiO_2	**E**	SnO_2
Formula of chloride	$SiCl_4$	**F**	$SnCl_4$
Reaction with acid	None	**G**	Slow

1.1 Mendeleev left gaps in his periodic table. Suggest why.

....

....

[1]

1.2 Predict properties **D** to **G**.

     D ....   **E** ....

     F ....   **G** ....

[4]

[Total 5 marks]

2 Before the development of the modern periodic table, scientists classified elements according to their atomic masses.

2.1 Why did early scientists use atomic mass and not atomic number?

....

....

[1]

2.2 Use the periodic table to identify two elements that would be in the wrong positions if the elements were ordered by atomic mass rather than atomic number.

....

[1]

2.3 How did the discovery of isotopes explain why atomic weights do not always give the correct order of elements?

....

....

[2]

[Total 4 marks]

Topic C1 — Atomic Structure and the Periodic Table

The Modern Periodic Table

1   Chemical elements are arranged in the periodic table.   (Grade 4-6)

1.1 How are the elements ordered in the periodic table?

....

[1]

1.2 Why is the table called the periodic table?

....

[1]

1.3 Why do elements in groups have similar chemical properties? Tick **one** box.

They have the same number of shells of electrons.   ☐

They have the same number of outer shell electrons.   ☐

They all have at least one full inner shell of electrons.   ☐

The atoms of the elements are similar in size.   ☐

[1]

[Total 3 marks]

2   **Figure 1** below shows the electronic configuration for a neutral atom of element **X**.   (Grade 6-7)

Figure 1

2.1 What group in the periodic table is element **X** in? Justify your answer.

....

....

[2]

2.2 Which period is element **X** in? Explain your answer.

....

....

[2]

2.3 Identify element **X**.

....

[1]

2.4 Name one element that will have similar chemical properties to element **X**.

....

[1]

[Total 6 marks]

Topic C1 — Atomic Structure and the Periodic Table

Metals and Non-Metals

1 Elements can be classified as metals or non-metals. Some metals will react with particular non-metals to form compounds made up of ions.

1.1 Two elements, with the chemical symbols A and X, react together to form a compound made up of A^{2+} ions and X^{2-} ions. One of the elements is a metal and one is a non-metal. State which element is the metal and which is the non-metal.

A^{2+} .... X^{2-} ....

[1]

1.2 Element Z is a non-metal. State three physical properties that element Z is likely to have.

....

....

....

[3]

[Total 4 marks]

2 Metals make up about 80% of all the elements in the periodic table. Aluminium and magnesium are both metals.

2.1 Describe where metals and non-metals can be found in the periodic table.

Metals: ....

Non-metals: ....

[1]

2.2 Which of the statements below is true? Tick **one** box.

Elements that react to form negative ions are metals. ☐

Elements that react to form positive ions are metals. ☐

Elements that react to form positive ions are non-metals. ☐

Elements that do not form ions are metals. ☐

[1]

2.3 Suggest one physical property that magnesium and aluminium have in common.

....

[1]

2.4 Explain why magnesium and aluminium react in a similar way.

....

....

[2]

[Total 5 marks]

Topic C1 — Atomic Structure and the Periodic Table

Group 1 Elements

1 Data for two alkali metals, **X** and **Y**, is shown in the table below.

	Melting Point / °C	Density / kg per m³
X	39	1532
Y	98	968

1.1 Given that melting point decreases as you go down Group 1, which metal has the lowest atomic number, **X** or **Y**? Justify your answer.

....

....

[2]

1.2 Construct a balanced equation for the reaction between **X** and water to form the hydroxide, **XOH**, and a gas.

....

[2]

1.3 **XOH** is soluble in water. State the pH of the solution formed: ....

[1]

[Total 6 marks]

2 The element francium is at the bottom of Group 1 in the periodic table. Grade **7-9**

2.1 Complete **Table 1** by predicting the radius and boiling point of francium.
Use the data in the table to help you.

Table 1

	Boiling Point / °C	Radius of atom / pm
Rb	687.8	248
Cs	670.8	265
Fr	....	....

[2]

2.2 Compare the reactivity of francium to caesium. Justify your answer using your knowledge of francium's electron arrangement.

....

....

....

[3]

2.3 Alkali metals react with phosphorus, P_4, to form ionic phosphides. Lithium reacts with phosphorus to form lithium phosphide Li_3P. Predict the formula of francium phosphide and write a balanced equation for the reaction of phosphorus and francium.

Formula: ....

Equation: ....

[3]

[Total 8 marks]

Topic C1 — Atomic Structure and the Periodic Table

Group 7 Elements

Write the following Group 7 elements in order of increasing boiling point.

Iodine

Bromine

Chlorine

Fluorine

....

....

....

....

1 The elements in Group 7 of the periodic table are known as the halogens. *(Grade 4-6)*

1.1 Which of the following statements about the halogens is true? Tick **one** box.

They are non-metals that exist as single atoms. ☐

They are metals that exist as single atoms. ☐

They are non-metals that exist as molecules of two atoms. ☐

They are metals that exist as molecules of two atoms. ☐

[1]

1.2 Compare the chemical reactivity of chlorine and bromine. Explain your answer.

....

....

....

[3]

1.3 Halogens can react with other elements to form molecular compounds. Of the following elements, suggest which one might form a molecular compound with chlorine. Tick **one** box.

Ca ☐   Cr ☐   Na ☐   P ☐

[1]

[Total 5 marks]

2 Halogens react with many metals to form metal halides. *(Grade 6-7)*
For instance, iron reacts with bromine to form iron bromide.

2.1 Complete and balance the following symbol equation for this reaction.

................Fe + ... $\rightarrow$ ....$FeBr_3$

[2]

2.2 Iron bromide is ionic. What is the charge on the bromide ion?

....

[1]

[Total 3 marks]

Topic C1 — Atomic Structure and the Periodic Table

3 Chlorine water was added to potassium bromide solution in a test tube and the contents shaken.

3.1 Complete the word equation below.

Chlorine + Potassium bromide → .... + ...

[1]

3.2 What would you observe when the two reactants are mixed?

....

[1]

3.3 Give the name for this type of reaction.

....

[1]

3.4 Will chlorine water react with potassium fluoride solution? Explain your answer.

....

....

[2]

[Total 5 marks]

4 This question is about the halogens. (Grade 7-9)

4.1 Describe the electronic structure of the halogens and how it changes down Group 7.

....

....

....

[2]

4.2 Hydrogen gas reacts explosively with fluorine, even at low temperatures, to form hydrogen fluoride, HF. Predict and explain how astatine might react with hydrogen. Include a balanced equation in your answer.

....

....

....

....

....

....

....

[5]

[Total 7 marks]

Exam Practice Tip

One of the most important things to learn about Group 7 elements is the trends you find as you go down or up the group. And you need to be able to explain these trends using the electronic structure of the halogens. Smashing.

Topic C1 — Atomic Structure and the Periodic Table

Group 0 Elements

1   The noble gases can be found in Group 0 of the periodic table.

   1.1   Using the information in Table 1, complete the table by predicting values for the boiling point of radon, the density of xenon and the atomic radius of argon.

Table 1

Element	Boiling Point / °C	Density / g/cm³	Atomic radius / pm
Ar	−186	0.0018	....
Kr	−152	0.0037	109
Xe	−108	....	130
Rn	....	0.0097	136

[3]

   1.2   Explain the chemical reactivity of krypton in terms of electron configuration.

     ....

     ....

[2]

   1.3   What is the difference between the electron configuration of helium and the rest of the noble gases?

     ....

     ....

[1]

[Total 6 marks]

2   Until 1962, no noble gas compounds existed. Since then, several noble gas compounds have been made. For instance, xenon difluoride exists as white crystals which are stable at room temperature in a dry atmosphere.

   2.1   Why were chemists surprised that a noble gas compound could be made?

     ....

[1]

   2.2   Why is it unlikely that iodine would form a compound with xenon?

     ....

[1]

   2.3   A liquid containing a mixture of neon and xenon was cooled down. One gas solidified at −249 °C and the other at −112 °C. Identify which noble gas solidified at −249 °C and which at −112 °C. Justify your answer.

     ....

     ....

     ....

[3]

[Total 5 marks]

Formation of Ions

1   This question is about atoms forming ions by losing or gaining electrons.   Grade 4-6

1.1   Which of the following statements about the atoms of metallic elements is correct?
Tick **one** box.

☐ Metal atoms usually lose electrons to become negative ions.

☐ Metal atoms usually gain electrons to become negative ions.

☐ Metal atoms usually gain electrons to become positive ions.

☐ Metal atoms usually lose electrons to become positive ions.

[1]

1.2   The diagram below shows the ions of four elements and four descriptions about where the elements can be found in the periodic table.
Draw lines to match each of the four ions to their description.

A^+	A non-metal from Group 6
D^-	A metal from Group 2
X^{2+}	A metal from Group 1
Z^{2-}	A non-metal from Group 7

[2]

[Total 3 marks]

2   This question is about sulfur atoms and sulfur ions.   Grade 6-7

2.1   Sulfur is in Group 6 of the periodic table. What is the charge on a sulfur ion?

....

[1]

2.2   Sulfur atoms have the electronic structure 2,8,6. Write out the electronic structure for a sulfur ion.
Explain your answer.

....

....

....

[3]

2.3   Name the element that has atoms with the same electronic structure as a sulfur ion.

....

[1]

[Total 5 marks]

Ionic Bonding

Choose from the formulas on the left to complete the table showing the dot and cross diagrams and formulas of various ionic compounds. You won't need to use all the formulas.

NaCl   MgCl$_2$ MgCl

Na$_2$O   NaO   NaCl$_2$

Dot and cross diagram	Ionic formula
$[Na]^+$ $[Cl]^-$	
$[Na]^+$ $[O]^{2-}$ $[Na]^+$	
$[Cl]^-$ $[Mg]^{2+}$ $[Cl]^-$	

---

1 Ionic bonding is one of the three types of chemical bonds found in compounds. *(Grade 4-6)*

1.1 In which of the following compounds are the particles held together by ionic bonds?
Put a tick in the boxes next to the **two** compounds that you think are ionic.

☐ calcium chloride   ☐ carbon dioxide   ☐ phosphorus trichloride

☐ potassium oxide   ☐ nitrogen monoxide

[2]

1.2 The dot and cross diagram below shows the formation of lithium fluoride from its elements. The diagram is incomplete. Complete the diagram by adding an arrow to show the transfer of electron(s), the charges of the ions and completing the outer shell electronic structure of the fluoride ion.

[3]

1.3 Name the force that holds the ions together in an ionic bond.

....

[1]

1.4 State how you can tell from a dot and cross diagram that the particles in a compound are held together by ionic bonds.

....

[1]

[Total 7 marks]

2 **Figure 1** shows the outer electronic structure of magnesium and oxygen.

Figure 1

2.1 Draw a similar diagram to show the electronic structures and charges of the ions that form when magnesium reacts with oxygen. You only need to show the outer shells of electrons.

[4]

2.2 Explain how an ionic bond forms when magnesium atoms react with oxygen atoms.

....

....

....

....

[4]

[Total 8 marks]

3 **Figure 2** is a representation of the structure of a compound formed from two unknown elements given the symbols X and Z.

Figure 2

$$\left[\begin{array}{c} X \end{array}\right]^{-} \left[\begin{array}{c} Z \end{array}\right]^{2+} \left[\begin{array}{c} X \end{array}\right]^{-}$$

3.1 Suggest which group in the periodic table each element is from and give a reason for your choice.

Element X: Group: ....

 Reason: ....

Element Z: Group: ....

 Reason: ....

[4]

3.2* Discuss the uses and limitations of dot and cross diagrams.

....

....

....

....

....

....

[6]

[Total 10 marks]

Topic C2 — Bonding, Structure and Properties of Matter

Ionic Compounds

Circle the correct words or phrases below so that the statement is correct.

In an ionic compound, the particles are held together by weak/__strong__ forces of attraction. These forces act __in all directions__/in one particular direction which results in the particles bonding together to form __giant lattices__/small molecules.

1 This question is about the structure and properties of ionic compounds. (Grade 4-6)

1.1 Which of the following properties is not typical for an ionic compound?
Tick one box.

◻ high melting and boiling points   ◻ conduct electricity in solution

◻ conduct electricity in the liquid state   ◻ conduct electricity in the solid state

[1]

1.2 Name the type of structure that ionic compounds have.

....

[1]

[Total 2 marks]

2 Sodium chloride is an ionic compound. (Grade 6-7)

2.1 Describe the structure of a crystal of sodium chloride. You should state:
- What particles are present in the crystal.
- How these particles are arranged.
- What holds the particles together.

....

....

....

....

[4]

2.2 Explain why sodium chloride has a high melting point.

....

....

[2]

[Total 6 marks]

3 Potassium bromide has a lattice structure that is similar to sodium chloride.

3.1 Complete the diagram below to show the position and charge of the ions in potassium bromide. Write a symbol in each blank circle to show whether it is a potassium ion or a bromide ion.

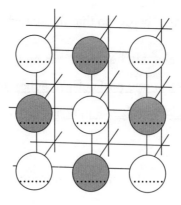

[3]

3.2 Give one advantage and one disadvantage of using the type of diagram above to represent the structure of an ionic compound.

Advantage: ....

Disadvantage: ....

[2]

3.3 What is the empirical formula of potassium bromide?

....

[1]

3.4 **Table 1** shows some data about potassium bromide. For each of the three properties shown in **Table 1**, explain how the structure of potassium bromide causes the particular property.

Table 1

Boiling point / °C	Electrical conductivity of solid	Electrical conductivity of solution
1435	Low	High

Boiling point ....

....

Electrical conductivity of solid ....

....

Electrical conductivity of solution ....

....

[6]

[Total 12 marks]

Exam Practice Tip

Don't panic if you're asked about an ionic compound that you've not met before. Think about what you *do* know about ionic compounds, and read the question carefully to make sure you've picked up any extra information you've been given.

Topic C2 — Bonding, Structure and Properties of Matter

Covalent Bonding

1   Some elements and compounds consist of molecules that are held together by covalent bonds.

   1.1   Describe how two atoms come together to form a single covalent bond.

....

                                                                                                            [1]

   1.2   What type of elements are able to form covalent bonds?

....

                                                                                                             [1]

   1.3   Borane is a compound that contains covalent bonds.
        Use the diagram below to find the molecular formula of borane.

Diagram:

Formula: ....

                                                                                                 [1]

                                                               [Total 3 marks]

2   The diagrams below show dot and cross diagrams of some simple covalent molecules. Draw out the displayed formulas of these molecules using straight lines to represent covalent bonds. One molecule (H_2) has been done as an example.

Dot and cross diagram   **Displayed formula**

H — H

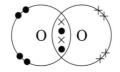

                                                                                                                     [Total 3 marks]

Topic C2 — Bonding, Structure and Properties of Matter

3 Methane, CH_4, is a covalent molecule. The structure of methane can be shown in a number of different ways. Two such diagrams are shown in **Figures 1** and **2**.

Figure 1

H
•×
H $\overset{}{\underset{×}{•}}$ C $\overset{}{\underset{×}{•}}$ H
•×
H

Figure 2

H
|
H—C—H
|
H

3.1 Suggest **two** different ways of telling, either from **Figures 1** and **2**, or from the molecular formula, that methane is a covalent molecule.

....

....

[2]

3.2 State **two** ways in which **Figures 1** and **2** do **not** represent a methane molecule accurately.

....

....

[2]

3.3 Briefly describe how the hydrogen atoms in a methane molecule are bonded to the carbon atom.

....

....

....

[3]

[Total 7 marks]

4 The structure of a covalent compound can be represented in many different ways. ⓖ 7-9

4.1 Give one advantage and one disadvantage of using each of the representations of covalent molecules described below.

Displayed formula: ....

....

Dot and cross: ....

....

3D Model: ....

....

[6]

4.2 Suggest, with reasoning, which of the representations in 4.1 would be most suitable for drawing the structure of a large polymer in order to show what each atom is connected to.

....

....

....

[2]

[Total 8 marks]

Simple Molecular Substances

1 This question is about the forces in simple molecular substances. $\overset{\text{Grade}}{\underset{4\text{-}6}{}}$

1.1 Compare the strength of the bonds that hold the atoms in a molecule together with the forces that exist between different molecules.

....

....

[2]

1.2 When a simple molecular substance melts, is it the bonds between atoms or the forces between molecules that are broken?

....

[1]

[Total 3 marks]

2 HCl and N_2 are both simple molecular substances. $\overset{\text{Grade}}{\underset{6\text{-}7}{}}$

2.1 Draw a dot and cross diagram to show the bonding in a molecule of HCl. Show all of the outer shell electrons and use different symbols for electrons from different atoms. There is no need to show inner shell electrons.

[2]

2.2 Draw a dot and cross diagram to show the bonding in a molecule of N_2. Show all of the outer shell electrons and use different symbols for electrons from different atoms. There is no need to show inner shell electrons.

[2]

2.3 State **one** difference between the bonding in HCl compared to N_2.

....

....

[1]

[Total 5 marks]

Topic C2 — Bonding, Structure and Properties of Matter

3 Iodine, I_2, is a simple molecular substance. **Grade 6-7**

3.1 At room temperature, iodine is a solid. Explain, with reference to the forces between molecules, why this is unusual for a simple molecular substance.

....

....

[2]

3.2 Predict, with reasoning, whether iodine can conduct electricity in any state.

....

....

[2]

[Total 4 marks]

4 Both methane (CH_4) and butane (C_4H_{10}) are simple covalent compounds that are gases at room temperature. Methane has a lower boiling point than butane. **Grade 7-9**

4.1 Explain, in terms of particles, what happens when methane boils and why the boiling point of methane is lower than that of butane.

....

....

....

....

....

....

[5]

4.2 Explain why a carbon atom can form up to four covalent bonds, whilst a hydrogen atom only ever forms one covalent bond.

....

....

....

[2]

4.3 Suggest how many covalent bonds an atom of silicon would form. Explain your answer.

....

....

[2]

[Total 9 marks]

Exam Practice Tip

Each atom in a molecule should have made enough covalent bonds to get a full outer shell. So to check that you've drawn your dot and cross diagrams correctly, count up how many electrons there are in the outer shell. Unless it's hydrogen, there should be eight electrons in the outer shell. Hydrogen should end up with two electrons in its outer shell.

Topic C2 — Bonding, Structure and Properties of Matter

Polymers and Giant Covalent Substances

Circle the diagram below that represents a compound with a giant covalent structure.

1 Graphite and diamond are compounds with very high melting points. `Grade 4-6`

1.1 Which of the following compounds is not an example of a giant covalent structure?
Tick **one** box.

☐ Ammonia ☐ Diamond ☐ Graphite ☐ Silicon dioxide

[1]

1.2 To melt a giant covalent compound, the covalent bonds between atoms must be broken.
Explain why this causes giant covalent compounds to have very high melting points.

....

....

[2]

[Total 3 marks]

2 **Figure 1** below represents a large molecule known as a polymer. `Grade 6-7`

Figure 1

2.1 What is the molecular formula of this polymer?

....

[1]

2.2 Is this molecule likely to be a solid, liquid or gas at room temperature? Explain your answer.

....

....

....

[3]

2.3 State what type of bonds hold the atoms in the polymer together.

....

[1]

[Total 5 marks]

Allotropes of Carbon

1 Carbon forms a number of different allotropes. **Grade 4-6**

1.1 One allotrope of carbon is diamond. Draw lines to connect each of the properties of diamond in the left hand column to the best explanation of that property in the right hand column.

Property

Does not conduct electricity

High melting point

Hard (doesn't scratch easily)

Explanation

Electrons in covalent bonds cannot move.

Each carbon atom makes four strong covalent bonds.

[2]

1.2 Name each of the allotropes of carbon, A-C, shown in **Figure 1**.

Figure 1

A   B   C

A ....   B ....   C ....

[3]

1.3 Suggest a use for allotrope C.

....

[1]

[Total 6 marks]

2 This question is about the carbon allotrope graphite. **Grade 6-7**

2.1 Describe the structure and bonding in graphite.

....

....

....

....

[4]

2.2 Graphite can be used to make components in electrical circuits.
Explain how the bonding and structure of graphite makes it suitable for this use.

....

....

[2]

[Total 6 marks]

Metallic Bonding

1 This question is about how the structure and bonding of metals affects their properties. Grade 6-7

1.1 Draw a labelled diagram to show how the metal particles and the electrons that take part in bonding are arranged in a metal.

[3]

1.2 Explain how the atoms are held together in this arrangement.

....

....
[2]

1.3 Explain whether this arrangement causes metals to generally have high or low boiling points.

....

....
[2]

1.4 Explain whether this arrangement causes metals to be good or poor conductors of electricity.

....

....
[2]
[Total 9 marks]

2 Metals are able to be bent and shaped. Grade 6-7

2.1 Explain how the structure and bonding in metals means they are able to be bent and shaped.

....

....
[2]

2.2 Alloys are mixtures of metals and a different element.
Explain why it is usually easier to change the shape of a pure metal than an alloy.

....

....

....
[3]
[Total 5 marks]

Topic C2 — Bonding, Structure and Properties of Matter

States of Matter

1 All substances can exist in three states of matter. (Grade 4-6)

1.1 Name the three states of matter.

....
[1]

1.2 Write the state of each substance next to each of the formulas below.

$NaCl_{(s)}$ ....

$O_{2(g)}$ ....

$Hg_{(l)}$ ....
[3]

[Total 4 marks]

2 Particle theory is a model used to explain how particles behave in the three states of matter. (Grade 6-7)

2.1 Describe how the particles in a substance are represented in particle theory.

....
[1]

2.2 Name the state of matter shown in **Figure 1**.

Figure 1

State: ....
[1]

2.3 Name two physical processes that particle theory can be used to explain.

....
[2]

2.4 Explain two ways in which particle theory doesn't accurately represent the particles in a substance.

....

....
[2]

[Total 6 marks]

Topic C2 — Bonding, Structure and Properties of Matter

Changing State

1 This question is about the processes by which a material changes state. **Grade 4-6**

1.1 What is the name of the process when a solid becomes a liquid?

....
[1]

1.2 What is the name of the temperature at which a liquid becomes a gas?

....
[1]

1.3 If a liquid turns into a gas at a very high temperature, what does this imply about the strength of the bonds between the particles in the substance?

....
[1]

[Total 3 marks]

2 Use the data in **Table 1** to help you answer the questions that follow: **Grade 7-9**

Table 1

Substance	Sodium Chloride	Water	Copper
Melting Point (°C)	801	0	1083
Boiling Point (°C)	1413	100	2567

2.1 Which substance in **Table 1** would be a liquid at 900 °C?

....
[1]

2.2 Which two substances would be gases at 1500 °C?

....
[2]

2.3 Which process requires the most energy: melting copper or boiling sodium chloride?

....
[1]

2.4 Does the data in **Table 1** suggest that the covalent bonds in a water molecule are weaker than the metallic bonds in copper? Explain your answer.

....

....

....

....
[4]

[Total 8 marks]

Topic C2 — Bonding, Structure and Properties of Matter

Relative Formula Mass

1   Match up the following formulas with the correct relative formula mass of the substance.

F_2	38
C_2H_6	40
CaO	30
NaOH	56

[Total 2 marks]

2   Magnesium oxide is a salt with the molecular formula MgO.

2.1   Calculate the percentage, by mass, of magnesium ions in magnesium oxide.
Relative atomic masses (A_r): O = 16,   Mg = 24

Percentage by mass of magnesium = ... %

[2]

2.2   A chemist is making a mixture that needs to contain 15% magnesium ions by mass.
Calculate the mass of magnesium in 200 g of this mixture.

Mass of magnesium = ... g

[1]

2.3   All the magnesium ions in the mixture come from magnesium oxide.
Using your answers to 2.1 and 2.2, calculate the mass of magnesium oxide needed to provide the
correct mass of magnesium ions in 200 g of the mixture.
(If you failed to get an answer to 2.1 or 2.2, you should use the percentage mass of magnesium as
40% and the mass of magnesium ions in the mixture as 20 g. These are **not** the correct values.)

Mass of magnesium oxide = ... g

[1]

[Total 4 marks]

The Mole

Warm-Up

The number of atoms, molecules or ions in 1 mole of a substance is given by the Avogadro constant. Tick the box next to the correct value of the Avogadro constant.

6.02×10^{-23} ☐ 0.62×10^{23} ☐ 6.20×10^{-23} ☐ 6.02×10^{23} ☐

1 Carbon dioxide (CO_2) and carbon monoxide (CO) can both be made by reacting carbon and oxygen. Relative atomic masses (A_r): C = 12, O = 16 *Grade 4-6*

1.1 Calculate the relative formula mass (M_r) of carbon dioxide.

M_r of carbon dioxide = ...
[1]

1.2 Calculate the number of moles in 110 g of carbon dioxide.

.... mol
[1]

1.3 Which would weigh more: 1 mole of carbon dioxide or 1 mole of carbon monoxide? Explain your answer using ideas about relative formula mass.

....

....
[2]

[Total 4 marks]

2 Iron and sulfur react together to form iron sulfide in the following reaction: *Grade 7-9*

$$Fe + S \rightarrow FeS$$

2.1 Calculate the mass of 2 moles of sulfur. Relative atomic mass (A_r): S = 32

Mass = ... g
[1]

2.2 Calculate the number of moles in 44 g of iron sulfide.
Relative atomic masses (A_r): Fe = 56, S = 32

.... mol
[2]

2.3 Which is greater, the number of atoms in 3 moles of sulfur or the number of molecules in 2 moles of iron sulfide? Explain your answer.

....

....

....
[2]

[Total 5 marks]

 ☐   ☐   ☐

Topic C3 — Quantitative Chemistry

124

Conservation of Mass

1 A student burned 12 g of magnesium in oxygen to produce magnesium oxide. *(Grade 4-6)*

1.1 Which of the following is the correctly balanced equation for the reaction between magnesium and oxygen? Tick **one** box.

$Mg + O \rightarrow MgO$ ☐ $2Mg + O_2 \rightarrow 2MgO$ ☐

$Mg + O_2 \rightarrow 2MgO$ ☐ $Mg + O_2 \rightarrow MgO$ ☐

[1]

1.2 The student measured the mass of magnesium oxide produced. The mass was 20 g. Calculate the mass of oxygen that reacted with the magnesium.

Mass of oxygen = ... g

[2]

[Total 3 marks]

2 This question is about conservation of mass. *(Grade 6-7)*

2.1 Explain what is meant by the term 'conservation of mass'. Give your answer in terms of the atoms that take part in a chemical reaction.

....

....

....

....

....

[3]

2.2 A student heated zinc powder in air. The equation for the reaction that happened is shown below.

$$2Zn_{(s)} + O_{2(g)} \rightarrow 2ZnO_{(s)}$$

The student weighed the mass of the powder before and after the reaction. Describe the change that would happen to the mass of the powder during the reaction. Explain this change using ideas from the particle model.

....

....

....

....

[3]

[Total 6 marks]

Topic C3 — Quantitative Chemistry

3 A student took some sodium carbonate powder and heated it in an open crucible. The equation for the reaction is: $Na_2CO_3 \rightarrow Na_2O + CO_2$

Grade 7-9

3.1 The student measured that the mass of the powder decreased during the reaction.
She concluded that the measurement must be wrong because mass is conserved during a reaction.
Explain whether the student's measurement or conclusion is likely to be correct.

....

....

....

....

....
[3]

3.2 The student calculated the relative formula masses (M_r) of the reactants and products.
The M_r of sodium carbonate was 106 and the M_r of carbon dioxide was 44.

Use these values to calculate the M_r of sodium oxide.

M_r of sodium oxide = ...
[1]

3.3 In the experiment, the student started with 53 g of sodium carbonate.
Calculate the mass of carbon dioxide that was produced.

Mass of carbon dioxide = ... g
[3]

3.4 Using the law of conservation of mass, calculate the mass of sodium oxide produced.

Mass of sodium oxide = ... g
[1]

[Total 8 marks]

Exam Practice Tip

There's a good chance that if you're given an equation in the exam and asked to do a calculation, you'll probably need to use the molar ratios in the equation. For example, in Q3.3, you need to work out the number of moles in 53 g of Na_2CO_3 and then use the molar ratios in the equation to work out the mass of CO_2.

Topic C3 — Quantitative Chemistry

The Mole and Equations

How many moles of O_2 are shown to be reacting in the equation below? Tick **one** box.

$$4Fe + 3O_2 \rightarrow 2Fe_2O_3$$

6 ☐   5 ☐   2 ☐   3 ☐

---

1   1 mole of sulfuric acid reacts with 2 moles of sodium hydroxide to form 1 mole of sodium sulfate and 2 moles of water.
Which of the following equations shows the reaction? Tick **one** box.

$2H_2SO_4 + NaOH \rightarrow 2Na_2SO_4 + H_2O$ ☐

$HCl + NaOH \rightarrow NaCl + H_2O$ ☐

$H_2SO_4 + 2NaOH \rightarrow Na_2SO_4 + 2H_2O$ ☐

$Mg + H_2SO_4 \rightarrow MgSO_4 + H_2$ ☐

[Total 1 mark]

2   9.2 g of sodium (Na) was reacted with 7.2 g of water (H_2O) to form sodium hydroxide (NaOH) and hydrogen (H_2).
Relative atomic masses (A_r): Na = 23, H = 1, O = 16

2.1   Calculate the number of moles of sodium that reacted with water.

.... mol
[1]

2.2   Calculate the number of moles of water that reacted with sodium.

.... mol
[2]

2.3   0.4 mol of sodium hydroxide and 0.2 mol of hydrogen were produced in the reaction.
Give the balanced symbol equation for the reaction between sodium and water.

Balanced symbol equation: .... + ... → .... + ...
[3]
[Total 6 marks]

3 Methane (CH_4) reacts with oxygen (O_2) to form carbon dioxide and water. Relative formula masses (M_r): $CH_4 = 16$, $O_2 = 32$, $CO_2 = 44$, $H_2O = 18$

Grade 7-9

3.1 A student carried out this reaction, reacting 8 g of methane with 32 g of oxygen, producing 22 g of carbon dioxide and 18 g of water.

Use these masses to work out the balanced equation for the reaction between methane and oxygen. Show your working.

Balanced symbol equation: .... + ... → .... + ...

[3]

3.2 The student repeated the reaction with 48 g of oxygen.
Calculate the number of moles of carbon dioxide that were produced.

.... mol

[3]

3.3 Another student carried out the reaction using 4 mol of methane.
Calculate the number of moles of water produced in this reaction.

.... mol

[1]

3.4 Calculate the mass of water produced in the reaction using 4 mol of methane.

Mass of water = ... g

[1]

[Total 8 marks]

Exam Practice Tip

If you're given the mass of a substance then you can use the formula linking mass, M_r and moles to calculate the number of moles. But remember, you can rearrange the formula too — so if you know how many moles of something you have, you can work out its mass, or if you know the mass and the number of moles you can work out its M_r. Cool eh?

Topic C3 — Quantitative Chemistry

Limiting Reactants

1 A student reacted excess calcium with hydrochloric acid. (Grade 4-6)

1.1 Explain why calcium was added in excess.

....

....

[1]

1.2 In this reaction, the hydrochloric acid is called the 'limiting reactant'.
Explain what this term means.

....

....

[2]

[Total 3 marks]

2 A student reacted copper oxide with sulfuric acid to make copper sulfate and water. (Grade 7-9)

$$CuO + H_2SO_4 \rightarrow CuSO_4 + H_2O$$

2.1 The student used 0.50 mol of sulfuric acid and an excess of copper oxide.
What mass of copper sulfate would be produced by the reaction?

Relative atomic masses (A_r): Cu = 63.5, S = 32, O = 16, H = 1

Mass of copper sulfate = ... g

[3]

2.2 The student decides to double the quantity of the sulfuric acid and use an excess of copper oxide.
Describe how this would affect the mass of the copper sulfate. Explain your answer.

....

....

[2]

2.3 The student found that only 0.4 mol of copper oxide was available
to react with the doubled quantity of sulfuric acid in question 2.2.
Explain the effect this would have on the amount of product obtained.

....

....

....

....

[3]

[Total 8 marks]

Concentrations of Solutions

1   28 g of calcium chloride was dissolved in 0.4 dm³ of water.

1.1 Calculate the concentration of the solution and give the units.

Concentration = ... Units = ...

[2]

1.2 Explain the term 'concentration of a solution'.

....

....

[1]

[Total 3 marks]

2   A student is preparing two solutions, A and B to use in an experiment.   Grade 6-7

2.1 To make solution A, he dissolves 40.0 g of a substance in 500 cm³ of a solvent.
     Calculate the concentration of solution A.

Concentration = ... g/dm³

[2]

2.2 Solution B needs to have a concentration of 60.0 g/dm³. What mass of the substance will the
     student need to dissolve in 500 cm³ to make solution B?

Mass = ... g

[1]

2.3 In the experiment, the student finds the concentration of a third solution, C.
     He repeats the experiment four times. The results of these repeats are
     18.2 g/dm³, 18.1 g/dm³, 18.4 g/dm³ and 18.5 g/dm³.
     Calculate the mean concentration of solution C.

Concentration = ... g/dm³

[1]

2.4 Estimate the uncertainty of your answer to 2.3.

Uncertainty = ± .... g/dm³

[2]

[Total 6 marks]

Acids and Bases

1   This question is about acids and bases. **Table 1** shows some everyday substances.

Table 1

Substance	pH
Beer	4
Bicarbonate of soda	9
Milk	7

1.1   Write the name of the substance in **Table 1** that is an acid.

....

[1]

1.2   What colour would you expect to see if Universal indicator was added to bicarbonate of soda solution?

....

[1]

1.3   Which ion is produced by an acid in aqueous solution?
Tick **one** box.

☐ Cl⁻   ☐ H⁺   ☐ OH⁻   ☐ OH⁺

[1]

1.4   State the range of the pH scale.

....

[2]

[Total 5 marks]

2   Acids and alkalis react together in neutralisation reactions.   (Grade 4-6)

2.1   Write the general word equation for a neutralisation reaction between an acid and an alkali.

....

[1]

2.2   In terms of hydrogen ions and hydroxide ions, write an ionic equation for a neutralisation reaction.

....

[1]

[Total 2 marks]

Strong Acids and Weak Acids

1 Below are some acids listed in order of strength.

Strongest ↑ Hydrochloric Acid

Nitric Acid

Citric Acid

Ethanoic Acid

Weakest ↓ Carbonic Acid

1.1 Hydrochloric acid is a strong acid while carbonic acid is a weak acid.
Explain the difference between a strong acid and a weak acid.

....

....

[2]

1.2 Describe and explain the difference you would expect to find in the pH value of a 1 mol/dm^3
solution of nitric acid and a 1 mol/dm^3 solution of ethanoic acid.

....

....

....

[3]

1.3 A 0.01 mol/dm^3 solution of hydrochloric acid has a pH of 2.
Predict the pH of a 0.001 mol/dm^3 solution of hydrochloric acid.

....

[1]

1.4 A solution of citric acid in a beaker has a pH of 3. Which of the following would increase the pH?
Tick **three** boxes that apply .

Adding citric acid with a higher concentration to the beaker. ☐

Adding water to the beaker. ☐

Adding ethanoic acid to the beaker at the same concentration as the citric acid. ☐

Adding hydrochloric acid to the beaker at the same concentration as the citric acid. ☐

Changing the citric acid to nitric acid of the same concentration. ☐

Changing the citric acid to carbonic acid of the same concentration. ☐

[3]

[Total 9 marks]

Exam Practice Tip

Make sure you understand what pH is and how it relates to the strength of an acid. It will also be jolly useful to understand how the concentration of H$^+$ changes with pH. Remember, don't confuse strong acids with concentrated ones.

 ☐   ☐   ☐

Reactions of Acids

1 Acids can react with bases and alkalis. (Grade 4-6)

1.1 What type of reaction occurs when an acid reacts with an alkali?
Tick **one** box.

☐ Oxidation ☐ Decomposition ☐ Neutralisation ☐ Precipitation

[1]

1.2 A student adds 2 spatulas of zinc carbonate into a beaker of dilute hydrochloric acid.
Draw **one** line to connect the observation you would expect during this reaction
with the explanation for that observation.

Observation	Explanation
Fizzing	Carbon dioxide is produced
A colour change	Hydrogen is produced
A white solid forming	A salt is made
No change	The zinc dissolves

[1]

[Total 2 marks]

2 Acids can react with metal oxides and metal hydroxides to give a metal salt and water. (Grade 6-7)

2.1 Write a word equation for the reaction of sulfuric acid and lithium hydroxide.

....

[2]

2.2 Complete and balance the symbol equation for the reaction of sulfuric acid and lithium hydroxide.

H_2SO_4 + ... LiOH → .... + ... H_2O

[2]

2.3 Acids can also react with metal carbonates. Compare the products of the reaction between
sulfuric acid and lithium carbonate with the products of the reaction between sulfuric acid and
lithium hydroxide.

....

....

[2]

[Total 5 marks]

Topic C4 — Chemical Changes

3   Soluble metal salts can be made from the reactions of acids and metal oxides.

3.1   Zinc chloride can be made from the reaction of zinc oxide and hydrochloric acid.
Describe a laboratory method to produce pure crystals of zinc chloride using this reaction.

....

....

....

....

....

....

....

[4]

3.2   Suggest an alternative to zinc oxide that would also react with
hydrochloric acid to form the desired product.

....

[1]

[Total 5 marks]

4*   A student is given three different unlabelled solutions. One contains sodium hydroxide, one contains sodium carbonate and one contains a sodium salt. Use your knowledge of chemical reactions to describe experiments that the student could do to decide which solution is which. Explain how your experiments would allow the student to identify the solutions. Clearly describe the reactants and products of any reactions you include.

....

....

....

....

....

....

....

....

....

....

....

....

[Total 6 marks]

Topic C4 — Chemical Changes

The Reactivity Series

1   Metals can be placed in order of reactivity based on how vigorously they react with acids. (Grade 4-6)

1.1   Write a word equation for the reaction of magnesium with hydrochloric acid.

....

[1]

1.2   What does the reaction of magnesium with hydrochloric acid produce? Tick **one** box.

Positive chloride ions ☐

Positive hydrogen ions ☐

Positive magnesium ions ☐

Negative magnesium ions ☐

[1]

1.3   Explain why iron reacts less vigorously with hydrochloric acid than magnesium does.

....

[1]

1.4   Name **one** metal that would react more vigorously with hydrochloric acid than magnesium does.

....

[1]

[Total 4 marks]

2   Some metals can react with water. (Grade 4-6)

2.1   Write the general word equation for the reaction of a metal and water.

....

[1]

2.2   Complete the symbol equation below, for the reaction of calcium and water. Include state symbols.

$$Ca_{(s)} + 2H_2O_{(l)} \rightarrow \text{.................} + \text{.................}$$

[2]

2.3   Suggest a metal which will react more vigorously with water than calcium. Explain your answer.

....

....

[2]

2.4   Put the metals sodium, zinc and potassium in order, based on how vigorously you think they would react with water.

Most vigorous .... Least vigorous

[1]

[Total 6 marks]

3 A student investigated the reactions of some metals and found the results shown in **Table 1**.

Table 1

Reaction	Observation
Lithium + water	Very vigorous reaction with fizzing, lithium disappears
Calcium + water	Fizzing, calcium disappears
Magnesium + water	No fizzing, a few bubbles on the magnesium
Copper + water	No fizzing, no change to copper
Iron + water	No fizzing, no change to iron
Lithium + dilute acid	Very vigorous reaction with fizzing, lithium disappears
Magnesium + dilute acid	Fizzing, magnesium disappears
Zinc + dilute acid	Fizzing, zinc disappears
Copper + dilute acid	No fizzing, no change to copper

3.1 Use the results in **Table 1**, along with your knowledge of the general reaction between an acid and a metal, to explain whether lithium or magnesium forms positive ions more easily.

....

....

....

[3]

3.2 Predict what the student would have seen if they had added sodium to water.

....

....

[2]

3.3 Put the metals calcium, copper and lithium in order from most reactive to least reactive.

....

[1]

3.4 Explain why it would be difficult to decide the order of reactivity of magnesium and zinc using these experiments. Suggest an experiment that could be used to decide which is most reactive.

....

....

[2]

[Total 8 marks]

Exam Practice Tip

Learning the order of the reactivity series could be really useful when it comes to answering questions in the exams. Try learning this mnemonic to help you remember... <u>P</u>apa <u>S</u>murf <u>L</u>ikes <u>C</u>alling <u>M</u>y <u>C</u>larinet <u>Z</u>any — <u>I</u>sn't <u>H</u>e <u>C</u>ute. (You don't have to use my Booker prize winning concoction, though. You could also make up your own.)

Topic C4 — Chemical Changes

Separating Metals from Metal Oxides

1 Most metals are found as compounds in ores in the earth. Some of the metals can be extracted from their ores by reduction with carbon.   *Grade 4-6*

1.1 Name a metal that can be found in the ground as an element.

....

[1]

1.2 Why are most metals found in the earth as compounds?

....

[1]

1.3 Define reduction in terms of the loss and gain of oxygen.

....

[1]

1.4 Explain why magnesium **cannot** be extracted from magnesium oxide by reduction with carbon.

....

....

[1]

[Total 4 marks]

2 Iron can be extracted by heating iron oxide, Fe_2O_3, with carbon. The reaction releases large amounts of heat so there is no need to continuously heat the reaction.   *Grade 6-7*

2.1 Write a symbol equation for a reaction between carbon and iron(III) oxide, Fe_2O_3.

....

[2]

2.2 For the reaction of iron(III) oxide and carbon to form iron, identify whether carbon has been reduced or oxidised. Explain your answer in terms of the transfer of oxygen.

....

....

[2]

2.3 Magnesium is extracted from magnesium oxide by reaction with silicon. A temperature of 1200 °C is required together with a reduced pressure.

Suggest why magnesium extraction is very costly when compared with iron extraction.

....

....

....

[2]

[Total 6 marks]

Redox Reactions

1 In a metal displacement reaction the least reactive metal is reduced. *(Grade 6-7)*

1.1 Define reduction in terms of electron transfer.

....
[1]

1.2 Which of the following reactions shows zinc being reduced?
Tick **one** box.

Copper nitrate + zinc → copper + zinc nitrate ☐

Zinc + oxygen → zinc oxide ☐

Zinc chloride + sodium → zinc + sodium chloride ☐

Zinc + hydrochloric acid → zinc chloride + hydrogen ☐

[1]

1.3 The equation shows the reaction of zinc with hydrochloric acid.

$$Zn_{(s)} + 2HCl_{(aq)} \rightarrow ZnCl_{2(aq)} + H_{2(g)}$$

Does hydrogen lose or gain electrons in this reaction?

....
[1]

1.4 What happens to chlorine in the reaction in 1.3?
Tick **one** box.

Chlorine is oxidised ☐

Chlorine is released ☐

Chlorine is reduced ☐

Chlorine is neither oxidised nor reduced ☐

[1]
[Total 4 marks]

2 A student reacts magnesium with an aqueous solution of iron chloride to produce magnesium chloride and iron. *(Grade 7-9)*
$$Mg_{(s)} + FeCl_{2(aq)} \rightarrow MgCl_{2(aq)} + Fe_{(s)}$$

2.1 Write an ionic equation for this reaction.

....
[1]

2.2 A student repeats the experiment with copper instead of magnesium.
State whether a reaction would still occur. Explain your answer.

....

....
[2]
[Total 3 marks]

Topic C4 — Chemical Changes

Electrolysis

Place the labels on the correct label lines to identify the parts of an electrochemical cell.

Anode   Electrolyte

D.C. power supply

Cathode

Anions

Cations

1 Lead bromide can be electrolysed, using molten lead bromide as the electrolyte. Grade 4-6

1.1 What is an electrolyte?

....

[1]

1.2 Write the word equation for the electrolysis of lead bromide.

....

[1]

1.3 Explain why lead ions move towards the cathode and not the anode.

....

....

[2]

1.4 What ions move towards the anode? Give the chemical formula and charge of the ion.

....

[1]

1.5 Is the reaction at the anode oxidation or reduction?

....

[1]

1.6 Why does the lead bromide need to be molten? Tick **one** box.

So the ions can move to the electrodes ☐

So the electrons can be conducted through the substance ☐

So the electrodes don't corrode ☐

So there is enough heat for the reaction to occur ☐

[1]

[Total 7 marks]

Topic C4 — Chemical Changes

2 **Figure 1** shows the extraction of aluminium. Aluminium oxide is mixed with cryolite. This mixture is then melted and electrolysed. Metallic aluminium is made at the cathode.

Figure 1

Negative electrode — Positive electrode

Molten aluminium oxide and cryolite

A

2.1 What is the liquid labelled **A**?

....

[1]

2.2 What is the purpose of mixing the aluminium oxide with cryolite?

....

[1]

2.3 Why do the graphite electrodes need to be replaced regularly?

....

....

[2]

[Total 4 marks]

3 Aqueous iron chloride solution can be electrolysed using inert electrodes.

3.1 Write the names of the ions present in iron chloride solution.

....

[2]

3.2 Draw **one** line to connect the correct products at each electrode when iron chloride is electrolysed.

At the cathode

| Iron is discharged |

| Hydrogen is discharged |

| Chlorine is discharged |

At the anode

| Iron is discharged |

| Oxygen is discharged |

| Chlorine is discharged |

[1]

3.3 What is discharged at the anode when iron sulfate solution is electrolysed with inert electrodes?

....

[1]

3.4 Iron can be extracted from iron solutions by electrolysis but this is not the usual method. Why is electrolysis not the usual method of extracting iron?

....

....

[2]

[Total 6 marks]

Topic C4 — Chemical Changes

4   A student investigated the products of electrolysis of a variety of aqueous solutions using inert electrodes. **PRACTICAL**

4.1 Draw a labelled diagram of suitable apparatus that could be used for these experiments.

[4]

4.2 Complete **Table 1** by predicting the products at the anode and cathode for each of the solutions.

Table 1

Solution	Product at cathode	Product at anode
$CuCl_2$		
KBr		
H_2SO_4		

[6]

4.3 When potassium nitrate solution is electrolysed neither potassium nor nitrogen are discharged. Explain why and state what is produced instead.

....

....

....

[4]

4.4 Write two half equations for the reaction that occurs when water is electrolysed.

Cathode: ....

Anode: ....

[2]

[Total 16 marks]

Exam Practice Tip

Electrolysis can be a hard subject to get your head around, and adding the electrolysis of aqueous solutions in to the mix doesn't make it any easier. But remember, in aqueous solution, different ions can be discharged depending on their reactivity. Make sure you know the different ions that can be removed from solution, and in what situations that will happen — it really isn't too complicated once you know what you are doing, but you do need to learn the rules.

Topic C4 — Chemical Changes

Exothermic and Endothermic Reactions

1   Which one of the following statements about exothermic and endothermic reactions is correct? Tick **one** box.   *(Grade 4-6)*

In an exothermic reaction, energy is transferred from the surroundings so the temperature of the surroundings goes down. ☐

In an endothermic reaction, energy is transferred from the surroundings so the temperature of the surroundings goes down. ☐

In an exothermic reaction, energy is transferred from the surroundings so the temperature of the surroundings goes up. ☐

In an endothermic reaction, energy is transferred from the surroundings so the temperature of the surroundings goes up. ☐

[Total 1 mark]

2   During a reaction between solutions of citric acid and sodium hydrogen carbonate, the temperature of the reaction mixture fell from 18 °C to 4 °C.   *(Grade 4-6)*

2.1   Is this reaction exothermic or endothermic?

....

[1]

2.2   Complete the reaction profile for this reaction to show how the energy changes as the reactants form the products. Mark the overall energy change on the diagram.

[2]

2.3   Where is the energy being transferred from in this type of reaction?

....

[1]

2.4   What happens to the amount of energy in the universe after the reaction?

....

[1]

2.5   Give a practical use of this type of reaction.

....

[1]

[Total 6 marks]

3 A company is trying to find a reaction with a low activation energy to use in a hand warmer. The reaction profiles for the reactions being investigated are shown in **Figure 1**.

Figure 1

3.1 Define 'activation energy' and describe how activation energy is shown on a reaction profile.

....

....

....

[2]

3.2 Suggest which reaction would be most suitable for using in a hand warmer. Explain your answer.

....

....

....

[3]

[Total 5 marks]

4 A student wanted to investigate how the choice of metal affects the temperature change of the reaction between a metal and an acid. Powdered samples of zinc, magnesium and copper are supplied, along with a solution of hydrochloric acid.

PRACTICAL

4.1 Suggest **three** essential pieces of apparatus needed for the investigation.

....

....

[3]

4.2* Describe a method for how the testing could be carried out.

....

....

....

....

....

....

[6]

[Total 9 marks]

Topic C5 — Energy Changes

Bond Energies

1 Methane and chlorine can react together as shown in **Figure 1**.
The bond energies of the substances in this reaction are shown in **Table 1**.

Figure 1

H—C—H with H on top and H on bottom + Cl—Cl ⟶ H—C—Cl with H on top and H on bottom + H—Cl

Table 1

Bond	Energy (kJ/mol)
C–H	413
Cl–Cl	243
C–Cl	346
H–Cl	432

1.1 Using the data in **Table 1**, calculate the energy change for the reaction.

Energy change of the reaction = ... kJ/mol

[3]

1.2 Explain, in terms of bond energies, whether the reaction is endothermic or exothermic.

....

....

[2]

[Total 5 marks]

2 Hydrogen and fluorine react together in the following way: $H_2 + F_2 \rightarrow 2HF$.
The overall energy change of the reaction is –542 kJ/mol.
The H–H bond energy is 436 kJ/mol and the F–F bond energy is 158 kJ/mol.

Calculate the energy of the H–F bond.

H–F bond energy = ... kJ/mol

[Total 3 marks]

Exam Practice Tip

The maths for bond energy calculations isn't too tricky — it's usually just simple addition, subtraction and multiplication, and you might need to rearrange an equation. But it's really, really easy to make a mistake — so take your time, work through the question carefully, and, if you've got time at the end of the exam, go back and check your answers.

Topic C5 — Energy Changes

Rates of Reaction

1   This question is about the rate of a chemical reaction between two reactants, one of which is in solution, and one of which is a solid.

1.1 Which of the following changes would **not** cause the rate of the chemical reaction to increase?
     Tick **one** box.

     Increasing the concentration of the solutions.   ☐

     Heating the reaction mixture to a higher temperature.   ☐

     Using a larger volume of the solution, but keeping the concentration the same. ☐

     Grinding the solid reactant so that it forms a fine powder.   ☐
                                                                                      [1]

1.2 What is the name given to the minimum amount of energy
     which particles must have if they are to react when they collide?

     ....
                                                                                      [1]

1.3 Explain why adding a catalyst to the reaction mixture, without changing any other condition,
     can cause the rate of the reaction to increase.

     ....
                                                                                      [1]
                                                                             [Total 3 marks]

2   **Figure 1** shows how the mass of gas lost from a reaction vessel
     changes over time, for the same reaction under different conditions.

Figure 1

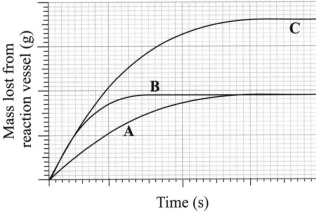

State which of the reactions, **A**, **B** or **C**:

Produced the most product: ....

Finished first: ....

Started at the slowest rate: ....
                                                                             [Total 3 marks]

Topic C6 — The Rate and Extent of Chemical Change

3 This question is about the rate of the reaction between magnesium and hydrochloric acid. The chemical equation for the reaction is:
$$Mg_{(s)} + 2HCl_{(aq)} \rightarrow MgCl_{2(aq)} + H_{2(g)}$$

3.1 The graph in **Figure 2** shows how the volume of hydrogen produced changes over the course of the reaction when a small lump of magnesium is added to excess hydrochloric acid.

On the same axes, sketch a curve to show how the volume of hydrogen produced would change over time if an identical piece of magnesium was added to excess hydrochloric acid with a higher concentration.

Figure 2

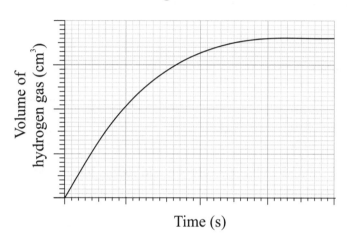

Time (s)

[3]

3.2 State **two** properties of the collisions between particles that affect the rate of a reaction.

....

....

[2]

3.3 Use collision theory to explain why increasing the concentration of a reactant increases the rate of the reaction.

....

....

[2]

3.4 How would you expect the reaction rate to change if the magnesium was cut into smaller pieces?

....

[1]

3.5 Explain why cutting the magnesium into smaller pieces affects the rate of this reaction.

....

....

[2]

3.6 State **one** change that could be made to change the rate of the reaction, other than changing the concentration and the size of the magnesium pieces.

....

[1]

[Total 11 marks]

Topic C6 — The Rate and Extent of Chemical Change

4 A student carries out a reaction between hydrogen gas and iodine gas to form hydrogen iodide (HI).

4.1 The student wants to increase the rate of the reaction, and decides to try two techniques:

1. Increasing the volume of the reaction vessel.
2. Increasing the temperature at which the reaction is carried out.

Explain, using collision theory, whether or not these changes will increase the rate of the reaction.

....

....

....

....

....

....

[5]

4.2 When cerium oxide is mixed with the hydrogen and iodine gases, the rate of the reaction increases. What does this suggest about cerium oxide?

....

[1]

4.3 State whether the reaction equation will change if cerium oxide is present in the reaction vessel. Explain your answer.

....

....

[2]

4.4 Sketch and label **two** reaction profiles on the axes below to show the difference between the reaction of hydrogen and iodine with and without cerium oxide. The energy of the products is lower than the energy of the reactants.

Energy

Progress of
Reaction

[3]

[Total 12 marks]

Exam Practice Tip

The key to explaining questions about reaction rates is usually collision theory. So if these questions are making you bang your head against your desk, have a read up on how collisions affect the rate of a reaction, and on how different reaction conditions influence these collisions. You'll thank me for it later, I can promise you.

Topic C6 — The Rate and Extent of Chemical Change

Measuring Rates of Reaction PRACTICAL

Warm-Up

Use the words on the left below to fill in the blanks of the passage on the right below.
No word is used more than once, but you may not need to use all the words.

products   mass

tangent

gradient   temperature

reactants

time   intercept

The rate of a reaction can be measured by dividing the amount of .... used up or the amount of .... formed by the .... To find the rate at a particular time from a graph with a curved line of best fit, you have to find the .... of the .... at that time.

---

1 To find the rate of a reaction you need to take measurements. Which of the following could you take measurements of to work out the rate of a reaction?

Grade 4-6

Tick **two** boxes.

Mass ☐   Volume of solution ☐

Volume of gas ☐   Frequency ☐

[Total 2 marks]

---

2 A student wants to investigate how the rate of a particular reaction is affected by temperature. The reaction produces a precipitate, so she plans to time how long it takes for the solution to go cloudy at each temperature.

Grade 4-6

2.1 What is the dependent variable in this experiment?

....

[1]

2.2 What is the independent variable in this experiment?

....

[1]

2.3 Suggest **one** variable that would have to be controlled in this experiment to make it a fair test.

....

[1]

2.4 The reaction also produces a gas. State whether it would be more accurate to measure the rate of the reaction by timing how long it takes for the solution to go cloudy, or by timing how long it takes a volume of gas to be produced. Explain your answer.

....

....

[2]

[Total 5 marks]

Topic C6 — The Rate and Extent of Chemical Change

3 The rate of a reaction was investigated by measuring the volume of gas produced at regular intervals. The results are shown in **Table 1**.

Table 1

Time (s)	0	60	120	180	240	300	360
Volume of gas (cm^3)	0.0	10.5	15.5	17.4	18.0	18.0	18.0

3.1 Name a piece of equipment that could be used to measure the volume of gas produced.

....
[1]

3.2 Plot the data in **Table 1** on the axes below. Draw a line of best fit onto the graph.

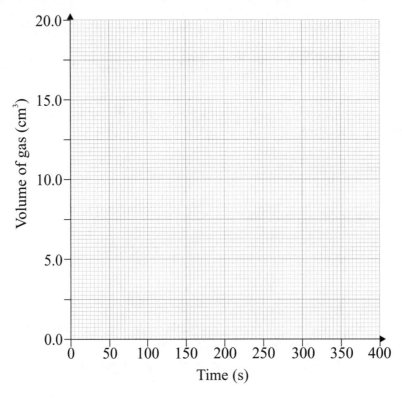

[3]

3.3 At what time does the reaction stop, according to your graph?

....
[1]

3.4 Calculate the mean rate of the reaction.

Mean rate of reaction = ...cm^3/s
[2]

3.5 Suggest how you could check whether the results are repeatable.

....

....
[2]

[Total 8 marks]

4 The rate of a reaction between two solutions was investigated by monitoring the amount of one of the reactants, A, at regular intervals. A graph of the results is shown in **Figure 1**.

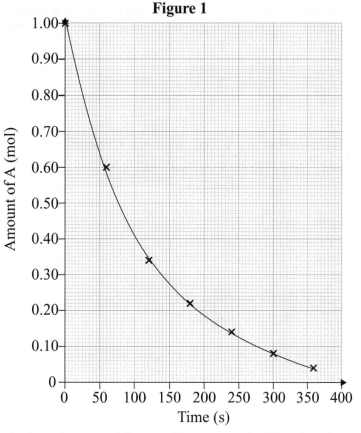

Figure 1

4.1 Use **Figure 1** to calculate the rate of the reaction at exactly 50 s after the start of the reaction. Give this rate to two significant figures. Include units in your answer.

rate = ... units = ...

[4]

4.2 In the same way calculate the rate of the reaction at exactly 200 s after the start of the reaction.

rate = ... units = ...

[4]

4.3 Describe and explain, with reference to collision theory, how the rate changes during the reaction.

....

....

[2]

[Total 10 marks]

Topic C6 — The Rate and Extent of Chemical Change

Reversible Reactions

1 This question is about the chemical reaction that is used to make ammonia from nitrogen and hydrogen. The equation for this reaction is: $N_2 + 3H_2 \rightleftharpoons 2NH_3$

Grade 4-6

1.1 What does the symbol '$\rightleftharpoons$' mean in this reaction?

....

[1]

1.2 When this reaction is carried out in a sealed container, it reaches equilibrium.
Which of the following statements about equilibrium is true?
Tick **one** box.

At equilibrium, all the reactants have reacted to form products. ☐

At equilibrium, the amount of products equal the amount of reactants. ☐

At equilibrium, the rate of the forward reaction
is equal to the rate of the backwards reaction. ☐

At equilibrium, both the forwards and the backwards reactions stop. ☐

[1]

[Total 2 marks]

2 An aqueous solution of blue copper(II) ions can react with chloride ions to form a yellow copper compound. The ionic equation for this reaction is: $Cu^{2+} + 4Cl^- \rightleftharpoons [CuCl_4]^{2-}$

Grade 7-9

2.1 The forward reaction is endothermic. What two things can you say about the enthalpy change for the reverse reaction?

....

....

[2]

2.2 A solution containing copper(II) ions is mixed with a solution containing chloride ions in a flask. The solution quickly turns green. When observed for a few minutes no further change in colour can be seen. Explain these observations.

....

....

....

[2]

2.3 Suggest **two** changes that could be made to the mixture that would change its colour.

....

....

[2]

[Total 6 marks]

Topic C6 — The Rate and Extent of Chemical Change

Le Chatelier's Principle

Predict whether the changes below would result in there being more reactants or more products at equilibrium for the reaction: $N_{2(g)} + 3H_{2(g)} \rightleftharpoons 2NH_{3(g)}$. The forward reaction is exothermic.

Increasing the temperature: ....

Decreasing the pressure: ....

Increasing the concentration of N_2: ....

1 The position of equilibrium of a reaction is dependent on the conditions that the reaction is carried out under. *Grade 4-6*

1.1 What does Le Chatelier's Principle say about the effect of changing the conditions of a reversible reaction at equilibrium?

....

[1]

1.2 State **two** conditions you could change in order to alter the position of equilibrium of a reaction that happens in solution.

....

....

[2]

[Total 3 marks]

2 A mixture of iodine monochloride (ICl) and chlorine is sealed in a gas syringe. The gases react in a reversible reaction to form iodine trichloride (ICl_3) and eventually reach an equilibrium. The equation for the reaction is: $ICl_{(l)} + Cl_{2(g)} \rightleftharpoons ICl_{3(s)}$. *Grade 6-7*

2.1 Given that the forward reaction is exothermic, explain how the relative quantities of ICl and ICl_3 would change if the mixture was heated, and all other conditions remained the same.

....

....

....

[2]

2.2 Explain how the relative quantities of ICl and ICl_3 would change if the plunger were pushed into the syringe, and the temperature remained constant.

....

....

....

[3]

[Total 5 marks]

Topic C6 — The Rate and Extent of Chemical Change

152

3 Dinitrogen tetroxide (N_2O_4) is a colourless gas. It decomposes in a reversible reaction to form the brown gas, nitrogen dioxide (NO_2). The reaction equation is: $N_2O_{4(g)} \rightleftharpoons 2NO_{2(g)}$. *(Grade 7-9)*

3.1 When a sample of N_2O_4 is left to decompose in a sealed tube, a pale brown colour can be seen. If this mixture is heated, the colour becomes a darker brown. Explain this observation and predict whether the forward reaction is exothermic or endothermic.

....

....

....

[3]

3.2 Explain how you would expect the colour of the equilibrium mixture to change if the pressure of the mixture is decreased, and all other conditions are kept the same.

....

....

....

[3]

[Total 6 marks]

4 Yellow iron(III) ions and colourless thiocyanate ions react reversibly in solution to form dark red iron thiocyanate: $Fe^{3+}_{(aq)} + SCN^-_{(aq)} \rightleftharpoons FeSCN^{2+}_{(aq)}$ *(Grade 7-9)*

The following observations are made about this reaction:
1. When a yellow solution containing Fe^{3+} ions and a colourless solution containing SCN^- ions are mixed, a pale red colour forms which initially grows darker but then stays constant.
2. When more Fe^{3+} ions are added to the solution it initially becomes more orangey in colour but then grows darker red than before the Fe^{3+} was added and remains like this.
3. If $FeSCN^{2+}$ ions are added to the solution it initially becomes darker in colour but then becomes more orangey.

Explain what is happening in each of these observations.

Observation 1: ....

....

Observation 2: ....

....

Observation 3: ....

....

[Total 6 marks]

Exam Practice Tip

Working out what happens to the position of an equilibrium when you change the conditions can be a bit of a brain twister. Just remember that for any change that's made, the reaction will try to do the opposite. So if you increase the temperature, more of the endothermic reaction will happen, if you increase the pressure, the equilibrium will move to the side where there are fewer moles of gas, and if you increase the concentration of a reactant, you'll get more products.

Topic C6 — The Rate and Extent of Chemical Change

Hydrocarbons

Place each of the compounds on the left, below in the correct column of the table depending on whether or not they are hydrocarbons.

propane   ethene

butanoic acid

C_2H_6 CH$_3$CH$_2$Cl

C_2H_4 hydrochloric acid

Hydrocarbon	Not a hydrocarbon

1   Alkanes are a family of hydrocarbons.   (Grade 4-6)

1.1   What is a hydrocarbon?

....

[1]

1.2   Which of the following shows the first four alkanes in order of decreasing carbon chain length?
Tick **one** box.

Propane, ethane, butane, methane   ☐

Methane, ethane, propane, butane   ☐

Ethane, methane, butane, propane   ☐

Butane, propane, ethane, methane   ☐

[1]

1.3   Write the general formula of alkanes in terms of *n*, where *n* is the number of carbon atoms.

....

[1]

1.4   Complete the word equation for the complete combustion of a hydrocarbon.

hydrocarbon + oxygen → .... + ...

[1]

1.5   During a combustion reaction, are the atoms in the hydrocarbon oxidised or reduced?

....

[1]

[Total 5 marks]

2 The molecular formulas for five hydrocarbons, **A** to **E**, are shown below. (Grade 4-6)

A C_4H_8 **B** C_4H_{10} **C** C_5H_{10} **D** C_5H_{12} **E** C_6H_{14}

2.1 Which hydrocarbon is butane?

....

[1]

2.2 Which of the hydrocarbons are alkanes? Explain your answer.

....

....

[2]

2.3 Which of the hydrocarbons is likely to have the highest boiling point? Explain your answer.

....

....

[2]

[Total 5 marks]

3 Petrol and diesel are both fuels containing mixtures of hydrocarbons. The average chain length of the hydrocarbons in petrol and diesel are different, which causes diesel to have a higher boiling point than petrol. (Grade 6-7)

3.1 Compare the viscosity of petrol and diesel.
Explain your answer with reference to the information above.

....

....

[2]

3.2 Predict whether petrol or diesel will be more flammable.
Explain your answer with reference to the information above.

....

....

[2]

3.3 Diesel contains alkanes that have 20 carbon atoms.
Give the molecular formula of an alkane with 20 carbon atoms.

....

[1]

3.4 Petrol contains alkanes with 8 carbon atoms.
Finish and balance the equation for the complete combustion of this hydrocarbon

.... C_8H_{18} + ... O_2 → .... + ...

[2]

[Total 7 marks]

Fractional Distillation

1 Crude oil is a finite resource. *(Grade 4-6)*

1.1 What is crude oil formed from?

....

[1]

1.2 What does 'finite resource' mean?

....

....

[1]

1.3 What type of substance does crude oil mainly consist of?
Tick **one** box.

Alkenes ☐

Alkanes ☐

Alcohols ☐

Water ☐

[1]

[Total 3 marks]

2 Fractional distillation is used to separate the mixture of molecules in crude oil into fractions such as petrol and diesel oil. *(Grade 6-7)*

2.1 What property of the molecules in crude oil is used to separate them into different fractions?

....

[1]

2.2 Explain how a fractionating column separates the molecules in crude oil into different fractions.

....

....

....

....

[3]

2.3 Fractions boil over a range of temperatures much narrower than the original crude oil.
What does this suggest about the structures of the hydrocarbons in a fraction?

....

[1]

[Total 5 marks]

Uses and Cracking of Crude Oil

1 Crude oil is processed to be used for a variety of purposes. (Grade 4-6)

1.1 Suggest **two** types of useful material produced from crude oil fractions.

....

[2]

1.2 Long-chain hydrocarbons can be processed to produce short-chain hydrocarbons.
What is the name of this process?
Tick **one** box.

Fractional distillation ☐

Thermal reduction ☐

Thermal oxidation ☐

Cracking ☐

[1]

1.3 Why do we break up long chain hydrocarbons into shorter chain hydrocarbons?

....

[1]

[Total 4 marks]

2 Some hydrocarbons from crude oil undergo processing by the petrochemical industry. For instance, decane, $C_{10}H_{22}$, can undergo cracking as shown in the following equation: (Grade 6-7)

$$C_{10}H_{22} \rightarrow C_8H_{18} + C_2H_4$$

2.1 What type of reaction is cracking?

....

[1]

2.2 Describe how cracking is carried out.

....

....

[2]

2.3 Cracking can form a variety of products.
Write an alternative balanced equation for the cracking of decane.

....

[1]

[Total 4 marks]

3 When large alkanes are cracked, smaller alkanes and alkenes are produced. An example of cracking is given in **Figure 1**.

Figure 1

C

3.1 Write the chemical formula of the reactant.

....
[1]

3.2 Draw the displayed formula of **D**.

[2]

3.3 Suggest a use for the alkene, **C**.

....
[1]

[Total 4 marks]

4* Explain why and how some fractions of crude oil are processed by cracking, giving chemical equations where relevant. You should state some uses of the products of this process.

....

....

....

....

....

....

....

....

....

....

[Total 6 marks]

Exam Practice Tip

When balancing cracking equations, make sure that there's at least one alkane and alkene in the products. Also, just like any chemical equation, remember to check that the number of each atom on both sides of the equations is the same.

Purity and Formulations

1   Copper can be made extremely pure. The melting point of two samples of copper were measured. Sample **A** had a melting point of 1085 °C and sample **B** melted over the range 900 – 940 °C.

1.1   How is a pure substance defined in chemistry? Tick **one** box.

A single element not mixed with any other substance.   ☐

A single compound not mixed with any other substance.   ☐

A single element or compound not mixed with any other substance.   ☐

An element that has not been reacted with anything.   ☐

[1]

1.2   Suggest which of the samples was the most pure? Explain your answer.

....

....

[2]

1.3   The boiling point of copper is 2,562 °C. Which of the samples is likely to have a boiling point closer to that of pure copper?

....

[1]

[Total 4 marks]

2   A paint was composed of 20% pigment, 35% binder, 25% solvent, and 20% additives.   ⟨Grade 6-7⟩

2.1   Explain why the paint is a formulation.

....

....

....

[3]

2.2   How would a manufacturer of the paint ensure that each batch had exactly the same properties?

....

[1]

2.3   Other than paint, name **one** other example of a formulation.

....

[1]

[Total 5 marks]

Exam Practice Tip

A formulation is a mixture but a mixture isn't always a formulation. For the exam, you may need to identify formulations based on information about their ingredients and how they've been designed to make the product fit for purpose.

Paper Chromatography

Warm-Up

Complete the diagram by correctly labelling the different parts of the chromatography apparatus using the labels on the left, below.

Watch glass

Sample

Filter paper

Baseline

Solvent

Spots of chemicals

1 Paper chromatograms were produced for three dyes, **D**, **E** and **F**, using a variety of solvents. The chromatogram produced using ethanol as a solvent is shown in **Figure 1**.

Figure 1

Solvent front

8.0 cm

9.5 cm

3.6 cm

D E F

1.1 Calculate the R_f values for **E** and **F** in ethanol, using the chromatogram shown in **Figure 1**.

R_f of **E** = ...

R_f of **F** = ...

[4]

1.2 Why do the substances travel different distances?

....

....

[1]

1.3 In all solvents, each dye only has one spot.
What does this imply about the composition of the dyes?

....

[1]

1.4 State which of the dyes could be the same.

....

[1]

[Total 7 marks]

Topic C8 — Chemical Analysis

2 A paper chromatography experiment was used to identify the compounds in a mixture, **W**, as shown in **Figure 2**. Three known compounds, **A**, **B** and **C** were spotted alongside **W**. Water was used as the solvent.

2.1 The experiment was conducted in a beaker with a watch glass functioning as a lid. Why is it necessary to have a lid while conducting a paper chromatography experiment?

....

[1]

2.2 The R_f values of **A** and **B** were found to be 0.9 and 0.1 respectively. With reference to the mobile phase and stationary phase, suggest why **A** has a much larger R_f value than **B**.

....

[1]

2.3 A diagram of the chromatogram from the experiment can be seen in **Figure 2**. State which of the known compounds could be found in **W**.

Figure 2

solvent front

spots of chemicals

baseline

W A B C

....

[1]

2.4 A student suggested that if the solvent was changed, the R_f value of compounds **A**, **B** and **C** would stay the same. Explain whether the student was correct.

....

....

....

[2]

2.5 The experiment was repeated again using a different solvent. The mixture **W** had three spots on the resultant chromatogram. What does this suggest about the mixture **W**?

....

[1]

2.6 Suggest why only two spots were shown on the chromatogram shown in **Figure 2**.

....

....

[1]

[Total 7 marks]

Exam Practice Tip

There are lots of different type of chromatography, but paper chromatography is the only one you need to know how to carry out. It's not just about knowing how to set up the apparatus — you also need to know how to analyse the results.

Topic C8 — Chemical Analysis

Tests for Gases

1   A student wants to identify a gaseous product.

The diagram below shows the gas being tested.

blue — A
white —
— gas being tested

1.1   Identify the item labelled **A** in the diagram.

....

[1]

1.2   Suggest which gas was present in the test tube.

....

[1]

[Total 2 marks]

2   A student performs an experiment that produces a colourless gas. She does not know what the gas is, so she collects it and tests it in order to identify it.

2.1   Suggest why the student should perform the experiment in a fume cupboard.

....

[1]

2.2   Describe how she could test the gas to see if it was carbon dioxide.

....

....

[2]

2.3   When a lighted splint is placed into a sample of the gas, it was **not** accompanied by a popping sound. What does this tell you about the gas?

....

[1]

2.4   When the student placed a glowing splint into a sample of the gas, the splint relighted. Identify the gas that was produced by her experiment.

....

[1]

[Total 5 marks]

Topic C8 — Chemical Analysis

Topic C9 — Chemistry of the Atmosphere

The Evolution of the Atmosphere

Circle whether each of the following sentences is **true** or **false**.

1) Earth's early atmosphere contained mainly nitrogen.	True or False
2) Earth's early atmosphere formed from gases released by volcanoes.	True or False
3) Earth's early atmosphere contained very little oxygen.	True or False
4) The oceans formed when oxygen reacted with hydrogen to form water.	True or False

1 The composition of gases in the atmosphere has varied during Earth's history. *(Grade 4-6)*

1.1 What are the approximate proportions of oxygen and nitrogen in the atmosphere today?
Tick **one** box.

One-fifth oxygen and four-fifths nitrogen. ☐

Two-fifths oxygen and three-fifths nitrogen. ☐

Three-fifths oxygen and two-fifths nitrogen. ☐

Four-fifths oxygen and one-fifth nitrogen. ☐

[1]

1.2 Other than oxygen and nitrogen, name **two** other gases in the atmosphere today.

....
[2]

1.3 How was the oxygen in the atmosphere produced?

....
[1]

1.4 How was nitrogen in the atmosphere produced?

....
[1]

1.5 For approximately how long has the atmosphere had a composition similar to what it is today?
Tick **one** box.

5 million years ☐   30 million years ☐   200 million years ☐   1 billion years ☐

[1]

[Total 6 marks]

2 During the Earth's first billion years, the percentage of carbon dioxide in the atmosphere was probably much higher than it is today. The formation of sedimentary rocks and fossil fuels helped to decrease the percentage of carbon dioxide.

2.1 Suggest **one** reason, other than sedimentary rock and fossil fuel formation, why the percentage of carbon dioxide in the atmosphere is thought to have decreased.

....

[1]

2.2 Outline how sedimentary rocks are formed.

....

....

[1]

2.3 State what the sedimentary rocks coal and limestone are formed from.

Coal: ....

Limestone: ....

[2]

[Total 4 marks]

3 There are several theories about how Earth's atmosphere evolved to its current composition. One theory suggests that the proportion of oxygen in Earth's early atmosphere was similar to the proportion in Mars' atmosphere today, which is 0.13%. The theory then suggests that, about 2.7 billion years ago, the proportion of oxygen in Earth's atmosphere started increasing.

3.1 Suggest why it's difficult to come up with a conclusive theory about how the atmosphere evolved.

....

[1]

3.2 Write a balanced symbol equation for the reaction that is thought to have caused the proportion of oxygen in Earth's atmosphere to increase.

....

[1]

3.3 Suggest why there is such a small amount of oxygen in the atmosphere of Mars.

....

....

[2]

3.4 Red beds are rocks that contain iron oxide. They form when other iron compounds from older rocks come into contact with oxygen in the atmosphere, and react. The oldest red beds formed about 2 billion years ago.

Suggest how this provides evidence for when the amount of oxygen in Earth's atmosphere started increasing.

....

....

[1]

[Total 5 marks]

Topic C9 — Chemistry of the Atmosphere

Greenhouse Gases and Climate Change

1 Greenhouse gases in the atmosphere help maintain life on Earth. *Grade 4-6*

1.1 Which of the following is **not** a greenhouse gas?
Tick **one** box.

Carbon dioxide ☐   Methane ☐

Nitrogen ☐   Water vapour ☐

[1]

1.2 State how greenhouse gases help to support life on Earth.

....

[1]

1.3 Give **two** examples of types of human activity which are leading to an increase in the concentration of greenhouse gases in the atmosphere.

....

....

[2]

[Total 4 marks]

2 An increase in the amount of greenhouse gases in the atmosphere may cause the climate to change. *Grade 6-7*

2.1 Explain how greenhouse gases help to keep the Earth warm.
Your answer should make reference to the interaction of greenhouse gases with radiation.

....

....

....

[3]

2.2 An increase in global temperatures could cause sea levels to rise.
Give **two** potential consequences of rising sea levels.

....

....

[2]

2.3 Other than rising sea levels, give **one** other potential consequence of climate change.

....

[1]

[Total 6 marks]

3* The global temperature anomaly is the difference between current temperature and an average value. The graph in **Figure 1** shows how the global temperature anomaly and the concentration of CO_2 in the atmosphere have varied over time. Describe the trends in the data and suggest reasons for them.

Figure 1

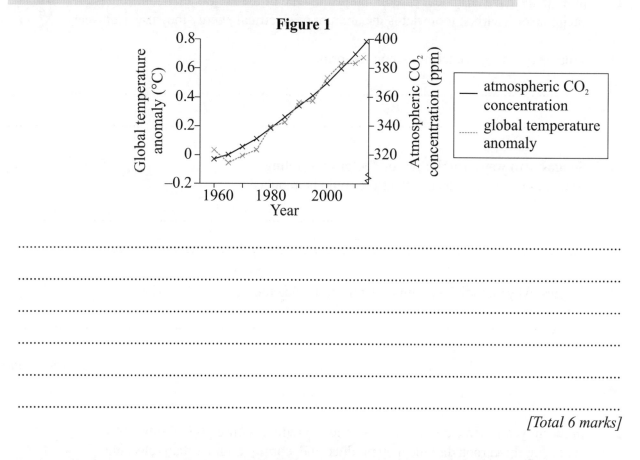

....

....

....

....

....

....

[Total 6 marks]

4 **Table 1** shows some data about atmospheric greenhouse gases. The global warming potential measures the impact of the gas on global warming compared to carbon dioxide.

Table 1

Gas	Formula	Current atmospheric level (%)	Lifetime in atmosphere (years)	Global warming potential
Carbon dioxide	CO_2	0.040	100-300	1
Methane	CH_4	0.00019	12	28
CFC-12	CCl_2F_2	5.3×10^{-7}	100	10 200

4.1 Use the table to suggest why methane is an important greenhouse gas, despite currently being at a lower level than carbon dioxide.

....

[1]

4.2 Use data from the table to explain why CFC-12 could have a significant impact on global warming.

....

....

[2]

[Total 3 marks]

Topic C9 — Chemistry of the Atmosphere

Carbon Footprints

1 Individuals have an annual carbon footprint. One of the factors that contributes to each person's carbon footprint is the amount of electrical energy they use each year.

Grade 4-6

1.1 What is meant by the term 'carbon footprint'?

....

....

[2]

1.2 Suggest **two** ways that the carbon footprint resulting from an individual's electricity usage could be reduced.

....

....

[2]

1.3 Suggest why an individual might not try to reduce their carbon footprint.

....

[1]

[Total 5 marks]

2 In recent years, some businesses have tried to reduce their carbon footprint by capturing the carbon dioxide they produce and storing it, rather than releasing it into the atmosphere.

Grade 6-7

2.1 Suggest **two** disadvantages for companies of capturing and storing carbon dioxide.

....

....

[2]

2.2 Discuss **two** ways in which governments can encourage businesses to reduce their carbon footprints and explain why some countries may be resistant to using these methods.

....

....

....

....

....

[4]

[Total 6 marks]

Exam Practice Tip

Learning the definitions for all the different terms that crop up in GCSE Science may be a bit of a bore, but it might be really useful in the exams. Learning all the itty bitty details is worth it if it means you get all the marks available.

Air Pollution

1 A variety of pollutants can be released when fuels burn, with a range of consequences. *Grade 4-6*

1.1 Why can the combustion of coal produce sulfur dioxide?

....

[1]

1.2 Name one pollutant that can lead to each of the following consequences:

Acid rain: ....

Global dimming: ....

[2]

1.3 State **two** ways in which acid rain can be damaging.

....

....

[2]

[Total 5 marks]

2 Combustion of fuel in cars is a major contributor to air pollution. *Grade 6-7*

2.1 Explain how cars produce nitrogen oxides.

....

....

[2]

2.2 Give **two** problems caused by nitrogen oxides in the environment.

....

....

[2]

2.3 Fuel combustion can produce particulates. What impact do particulates have on human health?

....

[1]

2.4 Combustion of fuels can also produce a gas that prevents blood from carrying oxygen around the body. Inhaling it can cause health problems, and sometimes death.

Name the gas and state why it is difficult to detect it.

....

....

[2]

[Total 7 marks]

Topic C10 — Using Resources

Finite and Renewable Resources

1   This question is about sustainable use of the Earth's resources.
Table 1 shows the time it takes to form various materials.

Table 1

Material	Time to form (years)
Wood	2-20
Coal	3×10^8
Cotton	0.5

   1.1   Using the data in **Table 1**, state **one** finite resource. Explain your answer.

....

....
[2]

   1.2   What is meant by the term 'renewable resource'?

....
[1]

[Total 3 marks]

2   Humans have developed items made from both natural and synthetic materials.

   2.1   Give **one** example of how agriculture is used to increase
the supply of an otherwise natural resource.

....

....
[1]

   2.2   Give **one** example of a synthetic product which has replaced
or is used in addition to a natural resource.

....
[1]

[Total 2 marks]

3   The mining of metals has economic, environmental and social impacts.

   Give **one** advantage and **one** disadvantage of metal mining.

....

....
[Total 2 marks]

Reuse and Recycling

1 This question is on sustainable development. **Grade 6-7**

1.1 What is sustainable development?

....

....

[2]

1.2 How do chemists play a role within sustainable development?
Explain your answer using an example.

....

....

....

[2]

[Total 4 marks]

2 Carrier bags can be made from a number of different materials. Two possible materials are jute and poly(ethene). **Table 1** gives some information about these materials. **Grade 6-7**

Table 1

	Poly(ethene)	Jute
Source	Crude oil	Plant fibre
Energy of Production	Moderate energy production	High energy production
Biodegradability	Not biodegradable	Biodegradable
Recyclability	Can be recycled	Possible but not widely done, likely to be reused

2.1 Using the information in **Table 1**, compare the sustainability
of the raw materials needed to make the bags.

....

....

[2]

2.2 Using the information in **Table 1**, compare the sustainability of the production of the bags.

....

....

[2]

2.3 Using the information in **Table 1**, compare the sustainability of the disposal of both bags.

....

....

....

[3]

[Total 7 marks]

Topic C10 — Using Resources

3 This question is on recycling. (Grade 6-7)

3.1 Give **two** reasons why recycling can be more sustainable than making new materials.

....

....
[2]

3.2 Name a material that is commonly recycled and briefly describe the process.

....

....
[2]

3.3 State **one** alternative to recycling that also improves sustainability.

....
[1]

[Total 5 marks]

4 This question is about the sustainability of copper. (Grade 7-9)

4.1 Explain how the process of phytomining is used to produce a substance
which contains copper compounds.

....

....

....

....
[4]

4.2 Describe **two** ways in which copper metal can be extracted from the product of phytomining.

....

....
[2]

4.3 Explain why phytomining cannot ultimately provide a sustainable source of copper metals.
Suggest **one** thing that can be done to make use of copper more sustainable.

....

....

....
[3]

[Total 9 marks]

Exam Practice Tip

Make sure you understand how reuse and recycling are used to make the materials we use in our daily lives
more sustainable. You should also get to grips with the different biological methods of extracting copper, and
the advantages in terms of sustainability of using these methods compared to traditional mining techniques.

Life Cycle Assessments

Draw one line between each stage of a product's life and the correct example of that stage.

Life cycle stage	Example
Getting the Raw Materials	Coal being mined from the ground.
Manufacturing and Packaging	Plastic bags going on to landfill.
Using the Product	A car using fuel while driving.
Product Disposal	Books being made from wood pulp.

1 Life cycle assessments are carried out on products as a way of finding out what their environmental impact is.
(Grade 6-7)

1.1 State **two** potential impacts of a product on the environment when it is disposed of at the end of its useful life.

....

....

[2]

1.2 Suggest **one** environmental consideration of a product which can be easily quantified while carrying out a life cycle assessment.

....

[1]

1.3 Suggest why some pollutant effects are less straightforward to quantify.

....

[1]

1.4 If two different assessors carried out a life cycle assessment on identical products, would you expect the results to be exactly the same? Explain your answer.

....

....

....

[3]

1.5 Some life cycle assessments can be selective in assessing the effects of a product on the environment. Explain how and why selective life cycle assessments could be misused.

....

....

[2]

[Total 9 marks]

Potable Water

For each of the statements below circle whether the statement is **true** or **false**.

1) Potable water does not contain any dissolved substances.

True or False

2) Potable water is the same as drinking water.

True or False

3) Potable water can only be produced from fresh water found in rivers, streams and reservoirs.

True or False

1   This question is about potable water. *Grade 4-6*

1.1 Which of the following is **not** a correct description of potable water? Tick **one** box.

Pure water ☐

Water containing a small number of microbes ☐

Water that is safe to drink ☐

Water with a low concentration of salt ☐

[1]

1.2 Fresh water is used to produce potable water. In the UK, where is the majority of fresh water sourced from during the production of potable water?

....
[1]

1.3 Draw **one** line between each treatment of water and the substances removed by the process.

Passing water through filter beds		Solid Waste
		Microbes
Sterilisation		Chemicals

[2]

1.4 Name **three** things that can be used to sterilise fresh water.

....

....
[3]

[Total 7 marks]

2 Distillation can be used to desalinate sea water. **Figure 1** shows a set of equipment that could be used to desalinate sea water.

 Grade 6-7

Figure 1

2.1 Name the components labelled **A** to **D** in the diagram.

A .... **B** ....

C .... **D** ....

[4]

2.2 Plan a method for using this equipment to produce a sample of potable water from seawater. You should include in your plan enough detail to allow someone to carry out the procedure safely and effectively.

....

....

....

....

....

[5]

2.3 Suggest a method, other than distillation, that could be used to desalinate water.

....

[1]

2.4 Explain why we do not use desalination to produce large quantities of potable water in the UK.

....

....

....

[2]

[Total 12 marks]

Exam Practice Tip

Some water costs a lot to make potable, some not so much. Make sure you understand the different processes that salty water and fresh water undergo to make it safe to drink and why the different processes are chosen.

Waste Water Treatment

1 Waste water must be treated before being reused or released into the environment. **Grade 4-6**

1.1 Which **two** of the following pollutants must be removed from sewage and agricultural waste water?

Calcium ions, Ca^{2+} ☐

Organic matter ☐

Harmful microbes ☐

Sodium ions, Na^+ ☐

[2]

1.2 Industrial waste water must have further treatment compared to sewage and agricultural waste water. Suggest why this.

....

[1]

[Total 3 marks]

2 This question is about the treatment of waste water in the form of sewage. **Grade 4-6** **Figure 1** shows a schematic diagram of a sewage treatment facility.

Figure 1

Waste Water → Screening → Sedimentation

Sedimentation — B → aerobic digestion → released into rivers

Sedimentation — A → **X** → natural gas / fertiliser

2.1 What is the purpose of the stage described as 'screening'?

....

....

[2]

2.2 What are the names given to the two substances produced by sedimentation?

Substance **A**: ....

Substance **B**: ....

[2]

2.3 What is the name of process **X**?

....

[1]

[Total 5 marks]

Topic C10 — Using Resources

 ☐ ☐ ☐

Energy Stores and Systems

1 **Figure 1** shows an apple on a tree. **Figure 2** shows a filament bulb connected to a battery. Both **Figure 1** and **Figure 2** show systems.

Figure 1

Figure 2

1.1 Define the term 'system'.

....

[1]

1.2 The apple in **Figure 1** falls from the tree.
Give **two** energy stores that energy is transferred between when this happens.

Energy is transferred from: ....

Energy is transferred to: ....

[2]

1.3 In **Figure 2**, energy is transferred from the chemical energy store of the battery to the thermal energy store of the bulb. State how energy is transferred between these two stores.

....

....

[1]

[Total 4 marks]

2* A cyclist allows his bike to roll down a hill without pedalling. Towards the bottom of the hill he applies his brakes. The bike comes to a stop. Applying the brakes causes the brakes to warm up. Describe the energy transfers that have occurred. State the forces doing work that cause each of these energy transfers. You can ignore any friction between the bike and the ground and any air resistance.

....

....

....

....

....

[Total 4 marks]

Exam Practice Tip

Make sure you know the different types of energy store and remember that energy transfers can occur mechanically (because of a force doing work, like above), electrically, by heating or by radiation (e.g. light and sound waves).

Kinetic and Potential Energy Stores

1 A student is tuning his guitar. He stretches the string by 10 mm so it produces the right note when played. The string has a spring constant of 20 N/m.

Calculate the energy stored in the elastic potential energy store of the string as it is stretched. You can assume that the limit of proportionality was not exceeded whilst it was being stretched. Use an equation from the Equations List.

Energy = ... J

[Total 2 marks]

2 A 0.1 kg toy contains a compressed spring. When the spring is released, the toy flies 0.45 m upwards from ground level, before falling back down to the ground.

Assuming there's no air resistance, calculate the speed of the toy when it hits the ground. Gravitational field strength = 9.8 N/kg.

Speed = ... m/s

[Total 5 marks]

3 Two children, A and B, fire identical 10.0 g ball bearings from a catapult. The elastic band of each catapult is elastically extended by 0.10 m and then released to fire the ball bearings.

3.1 Child A's elastic band has a spring constant of 144 N/m. Calculate the energy transferred to the kinetic energy store of child A's ball bearing. Use an equation from the Equations List.

Energy = ... J

[2]

3.2 The initial speed of child B's ball bearing is twice as fast as child A's ball bearing. Calculate the spring constant of child B's elastic band. Give your answer to 2 significant figures.

Spring constant = ... N/m

[5]

[Total 7 marks]

Specific Heat Capacity

Which of the following is the correct definition of specific heat capacity? Tick **one** box.

The energy transferred when an object is burnt. ☐

The maximum amount of energy an object can store before it melts. ☐

The energy needed to raise 1 kg of a substance by 10 °C. ☐

The energy needed to raise 1 kg of a substance by 1 °C. ☐

PRACTICAL

1   **Figure 1** shows the apparatus used by a student to investigate the specific heat capacities of various liquids. She measured out 0.30 kg of each substance, then supplied 15 kJ of energy to each sample using an immersion heater. She then recorded her results, shown in **Table 1**.

Figure 1

Table 1

Liquid	Mass (kg)	Temperature change (°C)	Specific heat capacity (J/kg °C)
A	0.30	12	4200
B	0.30	23	2200
C	0.30	25	....

1.1 Complete **Table 1** by calculating the specific heat capacity of Liquid C.
Use an equation from the Equations List.

[3]

1.2 Describe the energy transfers that occur when a liquid is heated using the equipment in **Figure 1**.

....

....

....

....

[4]

[Total 7 marks]

Exam Practice Tip

You may be asked about experiments you've never seen before in an exam, but don't panic. Take your time to read the experiment carefully and work out what's going on before attempting any questions to get full marks.

 ☐   ☐   ☐

Conservation of Energy and Power

Choose from the words on the left to fill in the blanks in the
sentences on the right. You do not need to use all of the words.

joules   work done
total   minimum
energy lost   rate of   watts

Power is the .... energy transfer or

.... It is measured in ....

1   An electric fan wastes some energy by transferring it to the thermal energy
stores of its surroundings. Describe what is meant by 'wasted energy'.

Grade 4-6

....

....

....

[Total 1 mark]

2   **Figure 1** shows a rechargeable battery-powered shaver. The shaver
transfers some energy to useful energy stores and wastes some energy.

Grade 4-6

Figure 1

2.1 Which statements about energy are false? Tick **two** boxes.

Energy can be transferred usefully.   ☐

Energy can be created.   ☐

Energy can be stored.   ☐

Energy can be dissipated.   ☐

Energy can be destroyed.   ☐

[1]

2.2 Give **one** example of a useful energy store and **one** of a wasted energy store that the shaver
transfers energy to.

Useful energy store: ....

Wasted energy store: ....

[2]

2.3 Describe what effect increasing the power of the shaver would have on the shaver's battery life.

....

[1]

[Total 4 marks]

3 A student is investigating the insulating properties of various materials. He surrounds a beaker of water with each material, before heating the water using an electric immersion heater with a constant power of 35 W. *(Grade 6-7)*

3.1 Write down the equation that links power, work done and time.

....
[1]

3.2 Calculate the work done by the immersion heater when it is operated for 600 s.

Work done = ... J
[2]

3.3 Whilst investigating the insulating properties of cotton wool, the student forgets to measure the time that he leaves the immersion heater on for. Calculate the time that the heater was on for, if it transferred 16 800 J of energy to the system.

Time = ... s
[2]

[Total 5 marks]

4 A car contains a worn out engine with a power of 32 000 W. The car takes 9.0 s to accelerate from rest to 15 m/s. A mechanic replaces the engine with a more powerful but otherwise identical one. The new engine has a power of 62 000 W. *(Grade 7-9)*

4.1 Explain how the new engine will affect the time it takes for the car to accelerate from rest to 15 m/s.

....

....

....

....
[3]

4.2 Calculate how long it will take for the car to accelerate to 15 m/s now. You can assume that the total amount of energy wasted whilst the car is accelerating is the same for both engines.

Time = ... s
[3]

[Total 6 marks]

Exam Practice Tip

For really big powers, you might see the unit kW, which stands for kilowatt. Don't let this put you off though, you just need to remember that 1000 W = 1 kW. You might see this in a few other units too, for example 1000 m = 1 km.

Topic P1 — Energy

Reducing Unwanted Energy Transfers

1 **Figure 1** shows a thermal image of a house. Different parts of the outside of the house are at different temperatures. The owner wants to keep the inside of the house as warm as possible.

Figure 1

Key

14 °C

5 °C

1.1 Suggest where the highest rate of unwanted energy transfer occurs in the house.

....

[1]

1.2 Suggest **one** way to reduce this unwanted energy transfer.

....

[1]

1.3 A second house is tested and it is found that the majority of its unwanted energy transfers occur around the doors and windows. Suggest **two** ways to reduce these energy transfers.

1. ....

2. ....

[2]

[Total 4 marks]

2 A builder is building an energy-efficient house.

She has four brick brands to choose from for the walls, shown in **Table 1**.

Table 1

Brand	Thermal conductivity (m²/s)	Brick thickness (cm)
A	5.2×10^{-7}	10
B	5.2×10^{-7}	15
C	2.7×10^{-7}	10
D	2.7×10^{-7}	15

Based on the information in **Table 1**, explain which brick brand she should use.

....

....

....

....

[Total 4 marks]

3 **Figure 2** shows an old-fashioned well. The handle is turned, which rotates the axle. This causes the rope attached to the bucket to wrap around the axle, raising the bucket from the well.

Figure 2

A student measures the time taken to raise a bucket of water from the well. After lubricating the axle of the well, the student repeats the test and finds the time taken is shorter. Explain why.

....

....

....

....

....

[Total 3 marks]

4 A student investigates which type of window is the best at reducing unwanted energy transfers. The student places different samples of windows on a hot plate and measures how long it takes for the top surface of the window sample to reach 30 °C.

Figure 3

glass   glass   glass   Thermal conductivity
air   air glass = 0.2 W/mK
Sample A   Sample B   Sample C   air = 0.03 W/mK

Figure 3 shows the cross-sections of each window sample. Rank them from best to worst for reducing unwanted energy transfers from a house. Explain your choices.

Best: ....   Second best: ....   Worst: ....

....

....

....

....

....

....

[Total 5 marks]

Topic P1 — Energy

Efficiency

1 20 kJ of energy is transferred to a mobile phone battery to fully charge it once it has lost all charge. It transfers 16 kJ of useful energy during use until it needs to be recharged. *(Grade 4-6)*

1.1 Write down the equation that links efficiency, total input energy transfer and useful output energy transfer.

....
[1]

1.2 Calculate the efficiency of the battery.

Efficiency = ...
[2]

[Total 3 marks]

2 An electric motor has a useful power output of 57 W and an efficiency of 75%. Calculate the total power input for the motor. *(Grade 4-6)*

Input power = ... W
[Total 3 marks]

3 A student investigates the efficiency of a scale model of an electricity generating wind turbine using the equipment in **Figure 1**. *(Grade 6-7)*

The student changes the number of sails on the turbine and measures the power output from the turbine's generator. The air blower is supplied with 533 W and has an efficiency of 0.62.

Figure 1

3.1 When using two sails, the efficiency of the turbine was 13%. Calculate the power generated. Give your answer to 2 significant figures.

Output power = ... W
[4]

3.2 Suggest **two** ways the student could increase the efficiency of the turbine.

1. ....

2. ....
[2]

[Total 6 marks]

Energy Resources and Their Uses

Warm-Up

Write the resources below in the correct place in the table to show whether they are renewable or non-renewable energy resources.

bio-fuel   oil

coal   hydroelectricity

solar

wind

nuclear fuel

tidal   geothermal

wave power   gas

Renewable	Non-renewable

1   Describe the difference between renewable and non-renewable energy resources. **Grade 4-6**

....

....

[Total 2 marks]

2   Most cars run on petrol or diesel, which are both derived from fossil fuels. **Grade 4-6**

2.1   Name the **three** fossil fuels.

....

[1]

2.2   Give **two** other everyday uses for fossil fuels.

1. ....

2. ....

[2]

2.3   Some modern cars are powered by bio-fuels. What are bio-fuels?

....

....

[1]

2.4   Suggest **one** reason why car manufacturers are developing cars that are powered by alternative fuels to petrol and diesel.

....

....

[1]

[Total 5 marks]

Topic P1 — Energy

3 A UK university is considering ways to reduce their energy bills. They are considering building either a single wind turbine nearby, or installing solar panels on top of their buildings. By commenting on the change of seasons throughout the year, suggest why the university may decide to install both wind turbines and solar panels.

Grade 6-7

....

....

....

....

[Total 5 marks]

4 An energy provider is looking to replace their old fossil fuel power plant. They are eligible for a government grant, so the initial building costs are negligible.

Grade 7-9

4.1* The energy provider is interested in building a power plant that uses renewable energy resources. They have narrowed their choice to either a hydroelectric power plant or a tidal barrage. Compare generating electricity from hydroelectricity and tides, commenting on their reliability and their impact on the environment.

....

....

....

....

....

....

[4]

4.2* An alternative is replacing the old power plant with a new power plant that is run on fossil fuels. Discuss the advantages and disadvantages of using fossil fuels to generate electricity.

....

....

....

....

....

....

....

....

....

[6]

[Total 10 marks]

Trends in Energy Resource Use

1   **Figure 1** shows the energy resources used to generate electricity in a country.

Figure 1

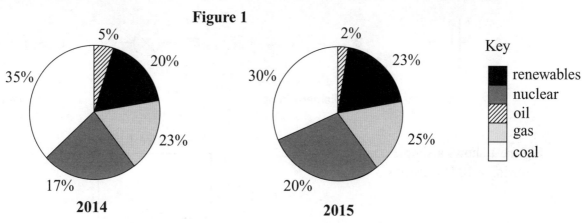

1.1   Determine what percentage of the country's electricity was generated by fossil fuels in 2014.

..........................%

[2]

1.2   Suggest **one** trend you can determine from the graphs in **Figure 1**.

....

[1]

[Total 3 marks]

2*   In the UK, the use of renewable energy resources is increasing, but many say it is not increasing at a fast enough rate. Suggest reasons for this increase in the use of renewable energy resources. Suggest and explain the factors that may affect the speed at which we use more renewable energy resources.

....

....

....

....

....

....

....

....

....

....

....

[Total 6 marks]

Topic P1 — Energy

Current and Circuit Symbols

Draw lines to match circuit symbols A-D to their correct names.

switch   filament lamp   fuse   cell

Figure 1

1   **Figure 1** shows a simple circuit, featuring a 10 Ω resistor.

$10\ \Omega$

1.1 Explain why there is no current in the circuit.

....
[1]

1.2 Use a word from the following list to complete the sentence below:

charge	potential difference	resistance	frequency

Current is the rate of flow of ....

[1]

[Total 2 marks]

2   **Figure 2** shows two ammeters, A_1 and A_2, in a circuit.
The reading on A_1 is 0.5 A.

Figure 2

2 V

A_1 X A_2

2.1 What is the reading on A_2?

Current = ... A
[1]

2.2 State the equation that links electric charge, time and current.

....
[1]

2.3 Calculate the charge that flows through component **X** in 2 minutes. Give the unit in your answer.

Charge = ... Unit = ...
[3]

[Total 5 marks]

Exam Practice Tip
You'll need to know the basics of how circuits work and the different circuit symbols for most electricity questions.

Resistance and V = IR

1 A current of 3 A flows through a 6 Ω resistor.
Calculate the potential difference across the resistor.

Potential Difference = ...V

[Total 2 marks]

PRACTICAL

2 A student investigated how the resistance of a piece of wire depends on its length.
The circuit she used is shown in **Figure 1**. Her results are displayed in **Table 1**.

Figure 1

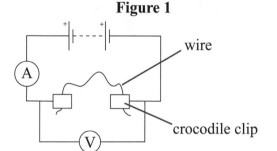

Table 1

Length / cm	Resistance / Ω
10	0.6
20	1.3
30	1.7
40	2.4
50	3.0

2.1 Describe how the student could have used the apparatus in **Figure 1** to obtain the results in **Table 1**.

....

....

[2]

2.2 Plot a graph of the data in **Table 1** on the grid shown in **Figure 2**.
Label the axes correctly. Draw a line of best fit on the graph.

Figure 2

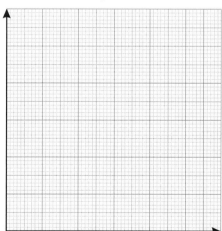

[4]

2.3 State **one** conclusion the student can make about the relationship between the resistance of a wire and its length. Explain how **Figure 2** shows this.

....

....

[2]

[Total 8 marks]

Topic P2 — Electricity

Resistance and I-V Characteristics

1   **Figure 1** shows some graphs of current against potential difference.

1.1   Tick the box below the correct graph for a resistor at constant temperature.

Figure 1

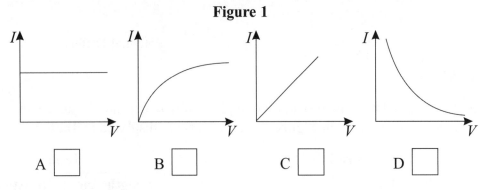

A ☐   B ☐   C ☐   D ☐
[1]

1.2   Name the type of graph shown in **Figure 1**.

....
[1]

1.3   Use words from the following list to complete the sentences below:

linear	non-linear	non-ohmic	ohmic

A resistor at a constant temperature is an example of a(n) ....

conductor. It is also an example of a(n) .... component.
[2]

[Total 4 marks]

2   This question is about diodes.

2.1   Draw the standard circuit symbol for a diode.

[1]

2.2   An old name for a diode is a valve. A valve in a bicycle pump only lets air flow through
      it in one direction. In what way do diodes behave in a similar way to valves?

....
[1]

2.3   A student measured the resistance of a diode using an electric circuit. He found the resistance
      to be 0.02 Ω. The next day he measured the diode again. This time he measured the resistance
      to be 100 MΩ. Suggest why the student's measurements were so different.
      You may assume that the circuit is working perfectly on both occasions.

....

....
[2]

[Total 4 marks]

PRACTICAL

3   A student used the circuit in **Figure 2** to find the *I-V* characteristic of a filament lamp.

Figure 2

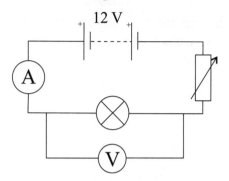

3.1 Explain the purpose of the variable resistor in the circuit.

....

....

[2]

3.2 The student obtained the graph displayed in **Figure 3**.
     Use the graph to find the resistance of the lamp at 3 A.

Figure 3

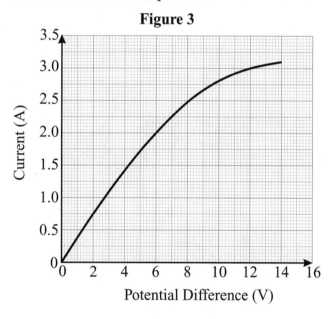

Resistance = ... Ω

[4]

3.3 What does the graph tell you about the lamp's resistance as the current increases?
     Explain why the resistance behaves in this way.

....

....

[2]

3.4 The student states that the lamp behaves as an ohmic conductor up to a potential difference of
     approximately 3.5 V. Explain what has led the student to this conclusion.

....

....

[2]

[Total 10 marks]

Topic P2 — Electricity

Circuit Devices

1   A student wants to measure the resistance of a light dependent resistor.

   1.1   Draw a circuit diagram (including an ammeter and a voltmeter)
       that can be used to measure the resistance of an LDR.

[3]

      The resistance of an LDR changes depending on its surroundings.

   1.2   State what happens to the resistance of an LDR as the surrounding light intensity increases.

....

[1]

   1.3   Give **one** example of a device that uses a light dependent resistor.

....

[1]

[Total 5 marks]

2   **Figure 2** shows a circuit that can be used for a light
      that lights up when the surface of a cooker is hot.
      Describe how the circuit works.

Figure 2

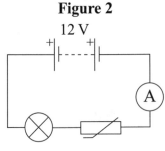

....

....

....

....

....

[Total 4 marks]

Exam Practice Tip

You may be asked to interpret the resistance graph of an LDR or thermistor. Remember the graph starts off steep and then
levels out. So for an LDR at low light intensities, a small change in light intensity will cause a large change in resistance.

Topic P2 — Electricity

Series Circuits

1 **Figure 1** shows a number of circuits.
Tick the box below the diagram that shows **all** the components connected in **series**.

Figure 1

A ☐   B ☐   C ☐   D ☐

[Total 1 mark]

2 In the circuit in **Figure 2**, the reading on the ammeter is 75 mA.

Figure 2

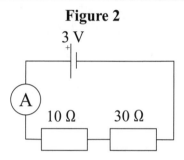

2.1 Calculate the total resistance of the two resistors.

Resistance = ... Ω

[1]

2.2 Find the potential difference across the 30 Ω resistor.

Potential Difference = ... V

[2]

[Total 3 marks]

3 In the circuit in **Figure 3**, the reading on the voltmeter is 2 V.
Component R is a resistor. Find the resistance of R.

Figure 3

Resistance = ... Ω

[Total 5 marks]

 ☐   ☐   ☐

Topic P2 — Electricity

Parallel Circuits

1   Draw a circuit diagram consisting of a cell and two filament lamps connected in parallel.

[Total 1 mark]

2   **Figure 1** shows a circuit with a 6 V supply and 4 Ω and 12 Ω resistors connected in parallel. There are also three ammeters and two voltmeters in the circuit.

Figure 1

2.1   Determine the readings on voltmeters V_1 and V_2.

Potential difference = ... V
[1]

2.2   Calculate the currents through A_1 and A_2.

A_1 current = ... A, A_2 current = ... A
[5]

2.3   Calculate the current from the supply as measured by A_3.

A_3 = ... A
[1]

[Total 7 marks]

3*   Explain why adding resistors in series increases the total resistance, whilst adding resistors in parallel decreases the total resistance.

....

....

....

....

....

....

....

[Total 6 marks]

Investigating Resistance

1 A student is investigating how adding identical fixed resistors in series affects the resistance of the circuit. **Figure 1** shows his results.

Figure 1

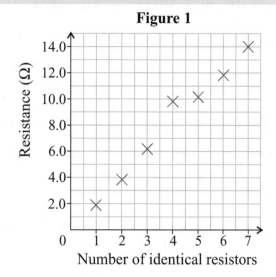

1.1 The student made a mistake when plotting his results. Draw a line of best fit for the student's data on **Figure 1**. Use this to predict the correct resistance for the incorrectly plotted result.

Resistance = ... Ω
[2]

1.2 The student repeats his experiment, this time using 1 Ω resistors.
Draw the predicted line of best fit for the results of this experiment on the axes in **Figure 1**.
[2]

[Total 4 marks]

2* A student wants to investigate how adding fixed resistors in parallel affects the overall resistance of a circuit. Describe an experiment the student could do to investigate this. You may draw a circuit diagram as part of your answer.

....

....

....

....

....

....

....

....

[Total 6 marks]

Electricity in the Home

Use the words given to complete the sentences about the wires in three-core cables.

| green and yellow | 0 | 230 | brown |

The live wire is .... and is at a potential difference of .... V.

The earth wire is .... and is at a potential difference of .... V.

1   A toaster is connected to the mains electricity supply using a three-core cable.   *Grade 6-7*

1.1   State the frequency and potential difference of the UK mains supply.

....

[2]

1.2* The toaster cable has a fault such that the live wire is in electrical contact with the neutral wire.
      Explain why the toaster will not work while this fault remains.

....

....

....

....

[4]

[Total 6 marks]

2   The cable that connects an iron to the mains supply has become worn with use. There is   *Grade 6-7*
        no insulation covering part of the live wire. The iron is plugged in, but switched off.

2.1   State **two** purposes of the insulation that covers the live wire.

....

....

[2]

2.2   A man switches on the iron and touches the exposed live wire. He receives an electric shock.
       With reference to the electrical potential of the man, explain why he receives an electric shock.

....

....

....

[3]

2.3   The socket is switched off and the iron is unplugged.
       Explain whether there is still a danger of the man receiving an electric shock from the plug socket.

....

....

....

[3]

[Total 8 marks]

Power of Electrical Appliances

1   Use the correct words from the following list to complete the sentences below.

current	power	in total	per second	potential difference	safety

The .... of an appliance is the energy transferred ....

Energy is transferred because the .... does work against the appliance's resistance.

[Total 3 marks]

2   A child is playing with a toy car. The car is powered by a battery and has two speed settings — fast and slow.

2.1   The child sets the speed to slow and drives the car for 20 seconds. The power of the car at this speed is 50 W. Write down the formula that links energy, power and time.

....

[1]

2.2   Calculate the energy transferred by the car.

Energy transferred = ... J

[2]

2.3   The child now sets the speed to fast. The power of the car at this speed is 75 W. Explain why the battery runs down more quickly when the car is set at a higher speed.

....

....

[2]

[Total 5 marks]

3   **Table 1** shows some data for two different cycles of a washing machine.

Table 1

Cycle	Power	Time needed
Standard Mode	600 W	125 minutes
Economy Mode	400 W	160 minutes

3.1   Name the **two** main useful energy transfers that take place in the washing machine.

....

....

[3]

3.2   Calculate the work done by the washing machine per minute when the machine is in Economy Mode.

Work done = ... J

[2]

3.3   Calculate the energy saved per cycle by using Economy Mode instead of Standard Mode.

Energy saved = ... J

[4]

[Total 9 marks]

Topic P2 — Electricity

196

More on Power

Warm-Up

Use the words below to fill in the gaps in the passage about energy in a circuit.

A power source supplies .... to a charge.

When a charge passes through a component with .... ,

it does .... , so the charge's energy ....

1 **Figure 1** shows a circuit. The reading on the voltmeter is 6 V and the reading on the ammeter is 2 A. This means 2 coulombs of electric charge pass through the ammeter every second.

Figure 1

1.1 Write down the equation that links potential difference, charge and energy transferred.

....

[1]

1.2 Calculate the energy transferred to lamp X when 2 C of charge passes through it.

Energy transferred = ... J

[2]

1.3 Explain why multiplying the current through lamp X by the potential difference across it will give you the same value as in 1.2.

....

....

....

[3]

[Total 6 marks]

2 Fans use a motor to turn a set of blades.

2.1 A 75 W ceiling fan in an office is powered by the mains supply at 230 V. Calculate the current supplied to the fan.

Current = ... A

[2]

2.2 A smaller fan on someone's desk runs from a computer's USB port. It has a power of 2.5 W, and draws a current of 0.50 A. Calculate its resistance.

Resistance = ... Ω

[2]

[Total 4 marks]

Topic P2 — Electricity

The National Grid

1   The national grid uses **transformers** to transfer energy efficiently.   Grade 4-6

1.1   Which **two** of the following quantities are changed by a transformer? (Assume the transformer is 100% efficient.) Put ticks in the boxes next to the correct answers.

☐ Power   ☐ Potential Difference   ☐ Current   ☐ Resistance

[2]

1.2   Describe the difference in the function of a step-up and a step-down transformer.

....

[1]

[Total 3 marks]

2   **Figure 1** shows a diagram of part of the national grid which transfers energy from a power station to a home.   Grade 6-7

Figure 1

Power Station → Transformer A → Power Cables → Transformer B → Home

2.1   What types of transformer are transformers A and B?

Transformer A = ...

Transformer B = ...

[2]

2.2*   Explain how transformer A helps to improve the efficiency of the national grid.

....

....

....

....

....

....

[4]

2.3   Explain the purpose of transformer B.

....

....

[2]

[Total 8 marks]

Exam Practice Tip

You don't need to understand how a transformer works, just what they're used for and the difference between them.

Topic P2 — Electricity

The Particle Model and Motion in Gases

The images below show the particles in a substance when it is in three different states of matter. Label each image to show whether the substance is a solid, a liquid or a gas.

  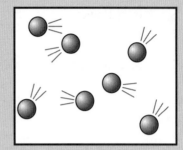

....

1   Use words from the box below to complete the passage. You can use each word **more than** once and you do not need to use all the words.

| potential | maximum | decreases | kinetic | increases | average |

When the temperature of a gas increases, the average energy in the .... energy

stores of the gas molecules increases. This .... the .... speed

of the gas molecules. If the gas is kept at a constant volume, increasing the temperature

.... the pressure.

[Total 3 marks]

2   A tyre is pumped up to its maximum volume. Grade 4-6

2.1 Using the particle model, explain what would happen to the tyre pressure if more air were pumped in, but its volume remained the same.

....

....

....

[3]

2.2 Explain why the tyre pressure would be higher on a hot day compared to a cold day.

....

....

....

....

....

[4]

[Total 7 marks]

3 Each container shown has the same mass of gas inside.
Tick the box below the container with the lowest gas pressure.

Volume = 0.04 m³
Temperature = 10°C

A ☐

Volume = 0.04 m³
Temperature = 20°C

B ☐

Volume = 40 000 cm³
Temperature = 20°C

C ☐

Volume = 40 000 cm³
Temperature = 30°C

D ☐

[Total 1 mark]

4 **Figure 1** shows a metal box that contains a gas at room temperature. The box has two lids
with different areas, that each require the same force in order to be removed from the box.
The box is heated using a hot plate. The temperature of the gas inside the box keeps rising
until, at a certain temperature, one of the lids will pop off the top of the box.

Figure 1

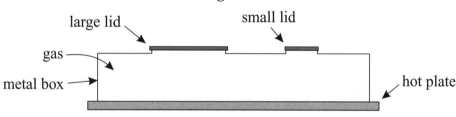

Explain why increasing the temperature of the gas causes a lid to pop off the box.
State which of the two lids will pop off first.

....

....

....

....

....

....

....

....

[Total 5 marks]

Exam Practice Tip

Make sure you can not only recognise particles in different states of matter (like the ones in the warm up question), but
that you can draw them too. This is especially useful when showing how the density of a material varies with its state.

 ☐   ☐   ☐

Density of Materials

1   A 0.5 m³ block of tungsten has a mass of 10 000 kg.   (Grade 4-6)

1.1   Write down the equation that links density, mass and volume.

....
[1]

1.2   Calculate the density of tungsten.

Density = ... kg/m³
[2]

1.3   Calculate the mass of a 0.02 m³ sample cut from the tungsten block.

Mass = ... kg
[2]
[Total 5 marks]

PRACTICAL

2*   A student has a mass balance, a measuring beaker and some acetic acid.   (Grade 4-6)

Describe an experiment the student can carry out to calculate the density of acetic acid, using the equipment listed.

....

....

....

....

....
[Total 4 marks]

PRACTICAL

3   A student uses the apparatus in **Figure 1** to calculate the densities of different rings to determine what materials they are made from.   (Grade 6-7)

Figure 1

eureka can   measuring cylinder

3.1 A eureka can is a beaker with a spout through which overflowing water can escape.
The can is filled up to the spout so that when an object is placed in the can the
displaced water flows into the measuring cylinder.
Describe how the apparatus in **Figure 1** could be used to determine the density of an object.

....

....

....

....

....

[4]

3.2 **Table 1** shows an incomplete table of the student's results.

Table 1

Ring	Mass (g)	Water displaced (ml)	Material
A	5.7	0.30	....
B	2.7	0.60	....
C	3.0	0.30	....

Complete **Table 1** using the following information:
Density of gold = 19 g/cm³   Density of silver = 10 g/cm³   Density of titanium = 4.5 g/cm³

[4]

[Total 8 marks]

PRACTICAL

4   A student investigates the density of an aluminium cola can by submerging it in a
measuring cylinder of water. When completely submerged, a full can of unopened cola
displaces 337 ml of water. The student then empties the can. She finds that it holds
332 ml of cola and that the mass of the empty can is 13.5 g when it is empty.
Calculate the density of aluminium used to make the can.

*Grade
6-7*

Density = ... g/cm³
[Total 4 marks]

Exam Practice Tip

You might be asked to explain an experiment that's used to find the density of an object. Make sure you know the
different equipment you would need for finding the density of a solid or a liquid and how the results are used.

Internal Energy and Changes of State

1 Use words from the box below to complete the passage.
You can only use a word **once** and you do not need to use all the words.

mass	increases	temperature	density	decreases

When a system is heated, the internal energy of the system .... This either

increases the .... of the system or causes a change of state. During a change of

state the temperature and .... of the substance remain constant.

[Total 2 marks]

2 A change of state is a physical change. **Grade 4-6**

2.1 State the name of the following changes of state:

Gas to liquid: .... Liquid to gas: ....

[1]

2.2 State what is meant by the term 'physical change'.

....

....

[1]

[Total 2 marks]

3 Heating an object increases its internal energy. **Grade 6-7**

3.1 State what is meant by the term 'internal energy'.

....

[1]

3.2 Heating an object can increase its temperature.
State **two** things that the increase in a system's temperature depends on.

1. ....

2. ....

[2]

[Total 3 marks]

4 A student fills a test tube with 30 g of water. He heats the water so that it begins to boil
and collects all of the water vapour produced via a tube placed into the bung of the test
tube. After the test tube has cooled, he finds that the mass of the water in the test tube is
now 20 g. State the mass of the water vapour the student collected. Explain your answer. **Grade 6-7**

....

....

....

....

[Total 2 marks]

Topic P3 — Particle Model of Matter

Specific Latent Heat

1 An immersion heater is used to boil 0.50 kg of water in a sealed container. *(Grade 6-7)*

1.1 Define the term 'specific latent heat'.

....

....
[1]

1.2 The lid is removed when the water begins to boil. The immersion heater transfers
1.13 MJ of energy to evaporate all of the water. Calculate the specific latent
heat of vaporisation of water. Use the equation from the Equations List.

Specific latent heat = ... MJ/kg
[3]

[Total 4 marks]

2 **Figure 1** shows a graph of temperature against time as a substance is heated. *(Grade 7-9)*

Figure 1

2.1 Describe what is happening during the period 3-8 minutes from the beginning of heating.

....
[1]

2.2 Explain, in terms of particles, why the graph is flat between 3-8 minutes even though the
substance is being heated.

....

....

....
[3]

2.3 Give the melting and boiling points of the substance.

Melting point = ... °C   Boiling point = ... °C   *[2]*

[Total 6 marks]

Topic P3 — Particle Model of Matter

Developing the Model of the Atom

What is the typical radius of an atom?

☐ 1×10^{-10} m   ☐ 1×10^{10} m   ☐ 1×10^{-20} m   ☐ 1×10^{-15} m

How many times smaller is the radius of a nucleus than the radius of the atom?

☐ 10   ☐ 10 000   ☐ 100   ☐ 1000

1   Our understanding of the structure of the atom has changed significantly since the early 19th century.   *Grade 4-6*

1.1   In 1804, Dalton believed that atoms were tiny spheres which could not be broken up.
State one way in which this model is different to our current understanding of atomic structure.

....

[1]

1.2   The alpha particle scattering experiment provided evidence for the nuclear model of the atom.
Name and describe the model that it replaced.

....

....

[2]

1.3   What did the work of James Chadwick prove the existence of around
20 years after the atomic nucleus became an accepted scientific theory?

....

[1]

[Total 4 marks]

2   Niels Bohr discovered that electrons within an atom can only exist with defined energy levels.   *Grade 4-6*

2.1   Describe how an electron can move between energy levels.

....

....

....

[2]

2.2   Name the type of particle created when an atom loses or gains electrons.

....

[1]

2.3   What is the charge on one of these particles if it is created by an atom losing an electron?

....

[1]

[Total 4 marks]

3* State **two** discoveries about atomic structure which arose from the alpha particle scattering experiment. In each case, state the observation that led to the discovery.

Grade
6-7

....

....

....

....

....

....

....

[Total 4 marks]

4 **Table 1** is an incomplete table showing the relative charges of the subatomic particles in an atom.

Grade
6-7

Table 1

Particle	Proton	Neutron	Electron
Relative charge	....	....	−1

4.1 Complete **Table 1**.

[2]

4.2 Describe how these subatomic particles are arranged in the atom.

....

....

....

[2]

4.3 An iron atom has 26 protons.
State the number of electrons in the atom and explain your reasoning.

....

....

....

[3]

[Total 7 marks]

Exam Practice Tip

Remember that nothing is ever completely certain — just look at John Dalton and his ideas about atomic structure. New experiments are taking place all the time and they can completely change our models and theories. Make sure you can describe how the nuclear model has changed and how this illustrates the fact that our theories can always change.

Topic P4 — Atomic Structure

Isotopes and Nuclear Radiation

Draw a line from each form of radiation to show how ionising it is.

| gamma | alpha | beta |

| moderately ionising | weakly ionising | strongly ionising |

1   Some isotopes are unstable. They decay into
more stable isotopes by emitting nuclear radiation.
Grade 4-6

1.1 What is the name of this process?

....

[1]

1.2 Describe what is meant by isotopes of an element.

....

....

[2]

1.3 Some nuclear radiation is ionising. Define ionisation.

....

[1]

1.4 An unstable isotope releases a particle made up of two protons and two neutrons from its nucleus.
Name this type of decay.

....

[1]

[Total 5 marks]

2   An isotope which emits alpha radiation is used in the circuit of a house's smoke
detector. Ionising radiation can be damaging if the human body is exposed to it.
Grade 6-7

Explain why the use of ionising radiation in the smoke detector does not pose a threat to the
health of people living in the house.

....

....

....

....

[Total 2 marks]

3 One isotope of sodium is $^{23}_{11}$Na. (Grade 6-7)

3.1 Write down the mass number of this isotope.

....

[1]

3.2 Calculate the number of neutrons in the sodium nucleus.

Number of neutrons = ...

[1]

3.3 Which of the following is another isotope of sodium? Tick one box.

$^{11}_{23}$Na ☐ $^{11}_{24}$Na ☐ $^{23}_{12}$Na ☐ $^{24}_{11}$Na ☐

[1]

3.4 An isotope of neon is $^{23}_{10}$Ne. Explain whether or not the charge on the neon isotope's nucleus is different to the charge on the nucleus of the sodium isotope.

....

....

....

[2]

[Total 5 marks]

4* Ionising radiation is used to detect leaks in pipes that are buried just below the ground. An unstable isotope is introduced to one end of the pipe and, above the ground, a radiation detector is moved along the path of the pipe. (Grade 7-9)

Explain how this method can be used to identify the location of a leak in the pipe, and suggest what type of radiation the isotope should emit.

....

....

....

....

....

....

....

....

....

[Total 6 marks]

Exam Practice Tip

If you're asked about uses of the different kinds of radiation, then think about their properties (how ionising they are, how far they travel etc.). Then just apply what you know to the situation — if you're trying to detect something from a long way away or through a thick barrier, then you want something which has a long range. Simple really...

 ☐   ☐   ☐

Topic P4 — Atomic Structure

Nuclear Equations

1 An electron is emitted from a nucleus. (Grade 6-7)

1.1 State the effect this has on the charge of the nucleus.

....
[1]

1.2 Explain the effect that this has on both the mass number and atomic number of the nucleus.

....

....

....
[3]

1.3 After emitting the electron, the atom is excited. It gets rid of excess energy by emitting a gamma ray. What effect does this have on the charge and mass of the nucleus?

....
[1]

[Total 5 marks]

2 A student writes down the following nuclear decay equation: $^{234}_{90}\text{Th} \longrightarrow ^{234}_{91}\text{Pa} + ^{0}_{0}\gamma$ (Grade 7-9)

2.1 Explain how you know that this equation is incorrect.

....
[1]

2.2 The student has missed out one other particle which is formed during this decay. Write down the symbol for this particle, including its atomic and mass numbers.

....
[1]

2.3 Radium (Ra) has atomic number 88. The isotope radium-226 undergoes alpha decay to form radon (Rn). Write a nuclear equation to show this decay.

....
[3]

2.4 The radon isotope then undergoes alpha decay to form an isotope of polonium (Po), which undergoes alpha decay to form an isotope of lead (Pb).
Calculate the number of neutrons in the nucleus of this lead isotope.

Number of neutrons = ...
[3]

[Total 8 marks]

Topic P4 — Atomic Structure

Half-life

1   The graph in **Figure 1** shows how the count-rate of a radioactive sample changes over time.

Figure 1

1.1   Define the term 'half-life' in terms of count-rate.

....

[1]

1.2   Using **Figure 1**, determine the half-life of the sample.

Half-life = ... s

[1]

1.3   Initially, the sample contains approximately 800 undecayed nuclei.
     Predict how many of these nuclei will have decayed after two half-lives.

Decayed nuclei = ...

[2]

1.4   After two half-lives, what is the ratio of the number of undecayed nuclei left to the initial number
     of undecayed nuclei? Tick **one** box.

1:2 ☐   2:1 ☐   1:4 ☐   4:1 ☐

[1]

[Total 5 marks]

2   **Table 1** shows data about two radioactive sources.

Table 1

	Isotope 1	Isotope 2
Number of undecayed nuclei	20 000	20 000
Half-life	4 minutes	72 years

Explain which isotope will have the highest activity initially.

....

[Total 1 mark]

Topic P4 — Atomic Structure

3 The activity of a radioisotope is 8800 Bq. After 1 hour and 15 minutes, the activity has fallen to 6222 Bq. A further 1 hour and 15 minutes after that, the activity has fallen to 4400 Bq.

Grade 6-7

3.1 Calculate the radioisotope's half-life. Give your answer in minutes.

Half-life = ... minutes

[1]

3.2 Calculate the activity of the isotope after a total time of 6 hours and 15 minutes has passed. Give your answer to 2 significant figures.

Activity = ... Bq

[2]

[Total 3 marks]

4 A radioactive sample has a 50 second half-life. The initial activity of the sample is 120 Bq.

Grade 7-9

4.1 Complete the graph in **Figure 2** to show how the activity will change in the first 150 seconds.

Figure 2

[Graph with Activity (Bq) on the y-axis, values 0, 20, 40, 60, 80, 100, 120; and Time (s) on the x-axis, values 0, 20, 40, 60, 80, 100, 120, 140, 160.]

[3]

4.2 Use your graph to predict the activity of the sample after 40 seconds.

Activity = ... Bq

[1]

4.3 Calculate a prediction of the activity after 250 s.
Explain why this prediction is less likely to be correct than your prediction in 4.2.

....

....

....

[3]

[Total 7 marks]

Topic P4 — Atomic Structure

Irradiation and Contamination

1   Workers in a nuclear power station take many precautions to prevent unnecessary exposure to radiation. Suggest **two** methods that could be used to reduce their exposure to radiation when dealing with highly radioactive substances.

Grade 4-6

1. ....

2. ....

[Total 2 marks]

2   A scientist is reviewing the safety procedures to be used in her lab. She is concerned about **contamination** and **irradiation**.

Grade 6-7

2.1   Explain the difference between contamination and irradiation.

....

....

....

....

[2]

2.2   Give **two** ways in which the scientist can protect herself against contamination when handling a radioactive sample with a low activity.

1. ....

2. ....

[2]

[Total 5 marks]

3*   Radium-226 is an alpha source that was used in clocks until the 1960s to make the hands and numbers glow. Explain whether a clockmaker should be more concerned about irradiation or contamination when repairing old clocks that contain radium.

Grade 7-9

....

....

....

....

....

....

....

....

[Total 6 marks]

Topic P4 — Atomic Structure

Contact and Non-Contact Forces

Write each word below in the table on the right
to show whether it is a scalar or vector quantity.

Scalar	Vector

acceleration   time   temperature

mass   weight   force

1 Which of the following correctly defines a vector? Tick **one** box. (Grade 4-6)

Vector quantities only have magnitude. ☐

Vector quantities show direction but not magnitude. ☐

Vector quantities have both magnitude and direction. ☐

Vector quantities are a push or pull on an object. ☐

[Total 1 mark]

2 A child is pulling a toy train along the floor by a piece of string.
State **one** contact force and **one** non-contact force that acts on the toy. (Grade 6-7)

Contact force: ....

Non-contact force: ....

[Total 2 marks]

3 **Figure 1** shows a pair of identical magnets. There is a force of repulsion between them. (Grade 6-7)

Figure 1

Magnet A   Magnet B

| S | N | | N→ | S |

3.1 Complete the diagram in **Figure 1** by drawing another arrow representing the force that magnet B exerts on magnet A.

[2]

3.2 Magnet B is replaced by a much stronger magnet but magnet A remains the same.
Describe how you would redraw the arrows on the diagram to show this new force interaction.

....

....

[2]

[Total 4 marks]

Weight, Mass and Gravity

1 Use words from the box below to complete the passage.
   You can only use a word **once** and you do not need to use all the words. Grade 4-6

| weight | kilograms | mass | directly | inversely | newtons | newton metres |

.... is the amount of matter in an object. .... is

a force due to gravity. Mass is measured in .... whilst weight is

measured in .... The weight of an object is ....

proportional to its mass.

[Total 3 marks]

2 What is meant by the term 'centre of mass'? Grade 4-6

....

....

[Total 1 mark]

3 The Opportunity rover is a robot which is currently on the surface of the planet Mars. Grade 6-7
   The total mass of the Opportunity rover and its landing parachute is 350 kg.

3.1 Write down the equation that links weight, mass and gravitational field strength.

....
[1]

3.2 Calculate the total weight of the Opportunity rover and its parachute when it was on the Earth.
     (The gravitational field strength of the Earth = 9.8 N/kg.)

Weight = ... N
[2]

3.3 When Opportunity landed on Mars it left behind its parachute and moved away to explore.
     The mass of the parachute was 209 kg. Calculate the weight of Opportunity without its
     parachute on Mars. (The gravitational field strength of Mars = 3.8 N/kg.)
     Give your answer to 3 significant figures.

Weight = ... N
[3]

[Total 6 marks]

Exam Practice Tip

Outside of physics, people often use the term weight when they mean mass. Make sure you get the differences straight in
your head. You measure mass in on a set of scales, but weight is a force measured by a spring-balance (newtonmeter).

Resultant Forces and Work Done

1   **Figure 1** shows four runners who are running in windy weather.
Tick the box under the runner who is experiencing the largest resultant force.

Figure 1

A ☐   B ☐   C ☐   D ☐

[Total 1 mark]

2   A woman pulls a 20 kg suitcase along a 15 m corridor using a horizontal force of 50 N.

2.1   Calculate the work done by the woman. Give the correct unit.

Work done = ... Unit = ...

[3]

2.2   Work has to be done against frictional forces acting on the wheels of the suitcase.
Explain the effect this has on the temperature of the suitcase.

....

....

[2]

[Total 5 marks]

3   **Figure 2** shows an incomplete free body diagram of a ladder leaning
against a wall. There is no friction between the ladder and the
wall but there is friction between the ladder and the ground.

Figure 2

→30 N

W ↓   ↑ 100 N

3.1   Using **Figure 2**, determine the weight of the ladder, W.

Weight = ... N

[1]

3.2   Complete **Figure 2** by drawing the missing frictional force.

[2]

[Total 3 marks]

Calculating Forces

Find the horizontal and vertical components of the force
shown on the right. Each side of a square equals 1 N.

Horizontal component = ... N

Vertical component = ... N

1 **Figure 1** shows a girl on a swing. Her weight of 500 N acts vertically downwards and
a tension force of 250 N acts on the ropes at an angle of 30° to the horizontal.

Figure 1

250 N

30°

500 N

Figure 2

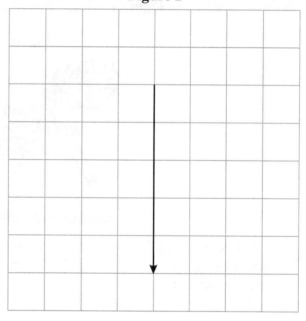

1.1 **Figure 2** shows an incomplete scale drawing for the forces acting on the girl.
Only the girl's weight has been drawn so far. Calculate the scale used in the drawing.

.... cm = ... N

[1]

1.2 Complete the scale drawing in **Figure 2** to find the
magnitude of the resultant force acting on the girl.

Magnitude = ... N

[2]

[Total 3 marks]

Topic P5 — Forces

Forces and Elasticity

1   Deformations can be elastic or inelastic.   (Grade 4-6)

1.1   Explain what is meant by the terms elastic deformation and inelastic deformation.

....

....

....

....

[2]

1.2   Stretching is one way in which forces can deform an object. State **two** other ways.

....

[1]

[Total 3 marks]

2   A student investigates the change in height of a toy horse in a playground, shown in **Figure 1**, when different people sit on it.   (Grade 7-9)

Figure 1

2.1   When a child weighing 250 N sits on the toy horse in **Figure 1**, his feet don't touch the floor. The height of the toy horse decreases by 20 cm. Calculate the spring constant of the spring. Give the correct unit.

Spring constant = ... Unit = ...

[3]

2.2   The child gets off and then the student's teacher then sits on the toy horse. Her weight is double that of the child. The student predicts that the height of the toy horse will change by 40 cm. Explain whether or not you agree with the student. State any assumptions you have made.

....

....

....

[2]

[Total 5 marks]

Investigating Springs

1   A student carried out an investigation to study the relationship between the force exerted on and the extension of a spring. He hung different numbers of 1 N weights from the bottom of the spring and measured the extension of the spring with a ruler, as shown in **Figure 1**.

Figure 1

ruler

clamp on clamp stand

1 N weights

Table 1

Force (N)	Extension (cm)
0	0
1	4.0
2	8.0
3	12.0
4	15.9
5	21.6
6	30.0

Figure 2

Extension (cm)

1.1   **Table 1** shows the results that the student obtained in his investigation.
Draw the force-extension graph for the student's results on the axes in **Figure 2**.

[3]

1.2   Using the graph you have drawn, calculate the spring constant of the spring being tested.

Spring constant = ... N/m
[2]
[Total 5 marks]

2   Calculate the work done on a spring when it is extended elastically by 8.0 cm. The spring constant of the spring is 25 N/m.

Work done = ... J
[Total 2 marks]

Exam Practice Tip

You need to know this practical really well — you could be asked pretty much anything about it in the exam. And make sure you draw graphs accurately with a sharp pencil. It'll really help if you need to use the graph to work something out.

Topic P5 — Forces

Distance, Displacement, Speed and Velocity

Choose from the words on the left to fill in the blanks on the right. Use each word once.

distance

velocity

vector

scalar

Displacement and .... are both

.... quantities. This means they have both a

size and a direction. Speed and .... are both

.... quantities. They do not depend on direction.

1   **Figure 1** shows the path taken by a football kicked by a child. When it is kicked at
Point A, the ball moves horizontally to the right until it hits a vertical wall at Point B.
The ball then bounces back horizontally to the left and comes to rest at Point C.

Grade 4-6

Figure 1

Scale 1 cm = 1 m

A   C   B

1.1 What is the distance that the ball has moved through from A to B?

Distance = ... m

[1]

1.2 What is the total distance that the ball has moved through from A to C?

Distance = ... m

[1]

1.3 Draw a vector arrow on **Figure 1** to show the displacement of the ball.

[1]

1.4 What is the magnitude of the displacement of the ball after it has come to rest?

Displacement = ... m

[1]

[Total 4 marks]

2   The speed of sound varies depending upon the substance
it is travelling through. State the speed of sound in air.

Grade 4-6

....

[Total 1 mark]

3   Give **three** factors that can affect a person's walking, running or cycling speed.

Grade 4-6

....

....

[Total 3 marks]

4 Explain whether a satellite orbiting the Earth at 3.07×10^3 m/s has a constant velocity. **(Grade 6-7)**

....

....

[Total 2 marks]

5 A man has just got a new job and is deciding whether to walk, cycle or take a bus to get to work. There are two routes he could take. The shorter route is along a 6 km path that only pedestrians and cyclists are allowed to use. The bus takes a longer route along a road. **(Grade 6-7)**

5.1 Write down the formula that links distance travelled, speed and time.

....

[1]

5.2 Estimate how long it would take the man to walk the pedestrian route.

Time taken = ... s

[3]

5.3 Estimate how much time would be saved if the man cycled this route instead.

Time saved = ... s

[4]

5.4 Travelling to work by bus takes 20 minutes.
The total distance covered during this time is 9.6 km.
Calculate the average speed of the bus.

Average speed = ... m/s

[3]

[Total 11 marks]

6 The speed at which an aircraft flies is often expressed in terms of its Mach number, which describes the speed in relation to the speed of sound. For example, Mach 2 is twice the speed of sound. A commercial airliner on a long-haul flight has a speed of Mach 0.8. The temperature of the air is typically –60 °C. **(Grade 7-9)**

The speed of sound is temperature dependent and can be found using:

Speed of sound in m/s = $331 + 0.6T$, where T is the temperature in °C.

Calculate the distance travelled by the jet over 5.0×10^4 s.

Distance travelled = ... km

[Total 4 marks]

Topic P5 — Forces

Acceleration

Draw one line from each scenario to the typical acceleration for that object.

A sprinter starting a race		10 m/s²
A falling object		2 × 10⁵ m/s²
A bullet shot from a gun		1.5 m/s²

1 Briefly describe the motion of a decelerating object.

....

[Total 1 mark]

2 **Table 1** shows how the speed of a car changes with time as it accelerates uniformly.

Table 1

Time (s)	0	1	2	3
Speed (m/s)	0	4	8	12

2.1 Write down the formula that links acceleration, velocity and time.

....

[1]

2.2 Calculate the acceleration of the car.

Acceleration = ... m/s²

[2]

[Total 3 marks]

3 A car accelerates uniformly at 2.5 m/s² from rest to a speed of 20 m/s. Calculate the time taken for the car to reach 20 m/s.

Time = ... s

[Total 3 marks]

4 A train travelling at 32 m/s slows down to 18 m/s over a distance of 365 m. Calculate the deceleration of the train over this distance. Use an equation from the Equations List.

Deceleration = ... m/s²

[Total 2 marks]

Distance-Time and Velocity-Time Graphs

1   A boat is being rowed along a straight canal. Some students use a watch to time how long after setting off the boat passes marker posts spaced 100 metres apart. **Table 1** shows their results.

Table 1

Distance (m)	0	100	200	300	400	500
Time (s)	0	85	165	250	335	420

Figure 1

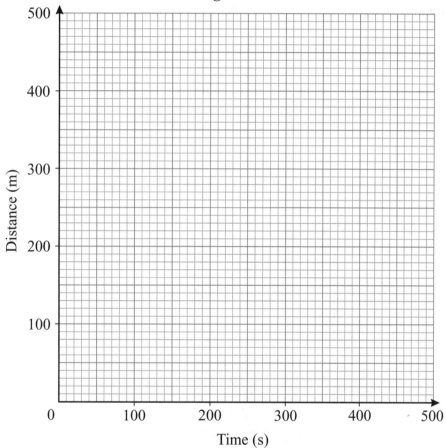

1.1 Draw the distance-time graph for the results in **Table 1** on the axes shown in **Figure 1**.

[3]

1.2 Using the graph in **Figure 1**, determine how far the boat travelled in 300 s.

Distance = ... m

[1]

1.3 Determine how long it took the boat to travel 250 m.

Time = ... s

[1]

1.4 Suggest **one** way to make the timings made by the students more accurate.

....

....

[1]

[Total 6 marks]

Topic P5 — Forces

2   **Figure 2** shows the distance-time graph for a cyclist's bike ride.   Grade 6-7

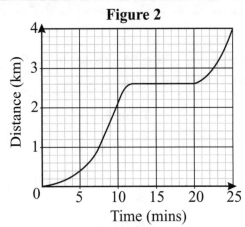

Figure 2

2.1   Use **Figure 2** to determine how long the cyclist rode for before stopping for a rest.

....

[1]

2.2   Describe the cyclist's motion in the first five minutes of her journey.

....

[1]

[Total 2 marks]

3   **Figure 3** shows the distance-time graph for a car's journey.   Grade 7-9

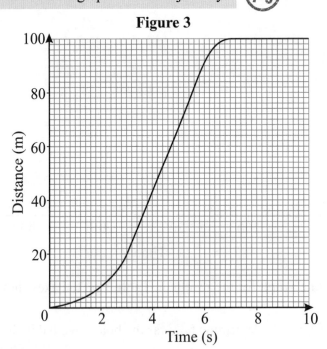

Figure 3

3.1   Use **Figure 3** to find the speed of the car 5 s into its journey.

Speed = ... m/s

[3]

3.2   Use **Figure 3** to find the speed of the car 2 s into its journey.

Speed = ... m/s

[3]

[Total 6 marks]

4   **Figure 4** shows an incomplete velocity-time graph for a roller coaster ride.

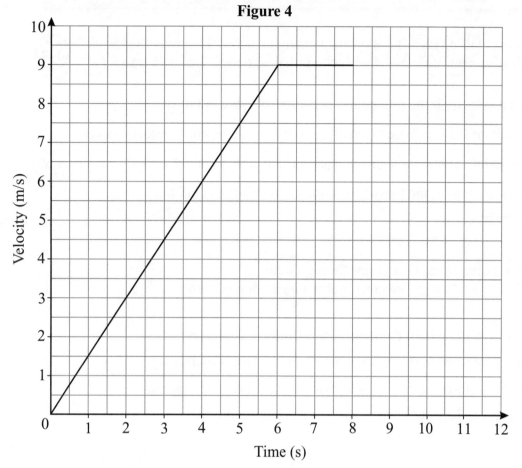

Figure 4

4.1 After 8 seconds, the roller coaster decelerates at an increasing rate.
    It comes to rest 4 seconds after it begins decelerating.
    Complete the velocity-time graph in **Figure 4** to show this.

[2]

4.2 Calculate the acceleration of the roller coaster during the first 6 seconds of the ride.

Acceleration = ... m/s^2

[2]

4.3 Calculate the distance travelled by the ride between 0 and 8 s.

Distance = ... m

[4]

4.4 Calculate the distance travelled during the entire ride to the nearest metre.

Distance = ... m

[5]

[Total 13 marks]

Topic P5 — Forces

Terminal Velocity

1 Any object falling (in a fluid) for long enough reaches its terminal velocity. (Grade 4-6)
Which statements correctly describe terminal velocity? Tick **two** boxes.

Terminal velocity is the minimum velocity an object can fall at. ☐

The resultant vertical force on an object falling at its terminal velocity is zero. ☐

The resultant vertical force on an object falling at its terminal velocity equals its weight. ☐

Terminal velocity is the maximum velocity an object can fall at. ☐

[Total 1 mark]

2 A fish is accelerating as it swims through water. (Grade 4-6)
Which of the following statements about its motion is true?

The resistive force from the water acting on the fish is constant. ☐

The resistive force from the water acting on the fish is increasing. ☐

The resistive force from the water acting on the fish is decreasing. ☐

There is no resistive force from the water acting on the fish. ☐

[Total 1 mark]

3 A student drops a large book and a cricket ball that (Grade 7-9)
both have the same weight from a tall building.

3.1 Explain why both objects eventually fall at a constant velocity.

....

....

....

....

[3]

3.2 Explain why the terminal velocity of the book is lower than the terminal velocity of the ball.

....

....

....

....

[2]

[Total 5 marks]

Exam Practice Tip

Remember that the acceleration of a falling object is continuously decreasing due to air resistance until it reaches zero.
That means you won't be able to use any of those fancy equations for uniform acceleration that you're used to.

Topic P5 — Forces

Newton's First and Second Laws

1 State Newton's First Law for a stationary object. (Grade 4-6)

....

....

[Total 1 mark]

2 Use words from the box below to complete the passage. You can only use a word **once** and you do not need to use all of the words. (Grade 4-6)

| area | mass | inversely | directly | resistive | resultant |

Newton's Second Law states that the acceleration of an object is ....

proportional to the .... force acting on the object and

.... proportional to the .... of the object.

[Total 3 marks]

3 **Figure 1** shows the horizontal forces acting on a motorbike travelling at a constant velocity. (Grade 6-7)

Figure 1

3.1 There are two resistive forces acting on the bike.
Suggest what these forces may be.

....

....

[2]

3.2 The engine provides a driving force of 5.0 kN. One of the resistive forces has a magnitude of 3.85 kN. Calculate the size of the second resistive force.

Force = ... N

[1]

[Total 3 marks]

4   A 5.0 kg vase is knocked from a shelf.

4.1   Write down the formula that links force, mass and acceleration.

....

                                                                        [1]

4.2   Calculate the resultant force acting on the vase as it begins to fall.
       Acceleration due to gravity, $g = 9.8$ m/s^2.

Force = ... N

[2]
[Total 3 marks]

5   A 1450 kg car accelerates uniformly from rest. It reaches 24 m/s in 9.2 s.
       Calculate the force needed to cause this acceleration.

Force = ... N

[Total 4 marks]

6   **Figure 2** shows a 7520 kg lorry. The driver spots a hazard ahead and applies
       the brakes. The lorry decelerates uniformly and comes to a stop 50 m after
       the brakes are applied. Estimate the braking force needed to stop the lorry.

Figure 2

50 m   7520 kg   F

Force = ... N

[Total 5 marks]

Exam Practice Tip

Watch out for questions talking about constant or uniform acceleration over a distance. They can be tricky and require a lot of steps. If you're struggling, read the question carefully, pick out the key bits of information and write them all down. Then look on the equation sheet to see if there are any equations you can use to find the values the question is asking for.

Inertia and Newton's Third Law

Which of the following is Newton's Third Law? Tick **one** box.

A non-zero resultant force is needed to cause a change in speed or direction. ☐

A resultant force is inversely proportional to the mass of an object. ☐

When two objects interact, they exert equal and opposite forces on each other. ☐

A resultant force of zero leads to an equilibrium situation. ☐

1   **Figure 1** shows the forces acting on a gymnast in equilibrium balancing on two beams.

Figure 1

320 N   320 N

640 N

1.1   State the force exerted by each of the gymnast's hands on the balance beams.

Force = ... N

[1]

1.2   State the name of this force.

....

[1]

1.3   State the size of the attractive force exerted on the Earth by the gymnast.

Force = ... N

[1]

[Total 3 marks]

2   Define the following terms: (Grade 6-7)

2.1   Inertia

....

[1]

2.2   Inertial mass

....

[1]

[Total 2 marks]

PRACTICAL

Investigating Motion

1   **Figure 1** shows the apparatus used by a student to investigate the effect of varying force on the acceleration of a trolley. The trolley is on a frictionless, flat surface.

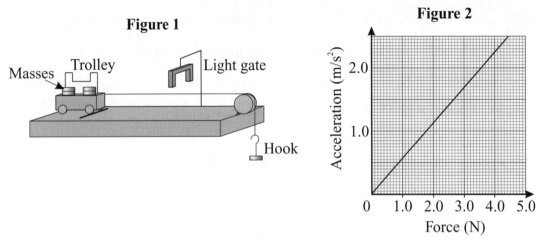

Figure 1

Figure 2

When the hook is allowed to fall, the trolley accelerates. The force acting on, and the acceleration of, the trolley are recorded. The student repeats this process, each time moving a 1.0 N mass from the trolley to the hook. **Figure 2** is a graph of acceleration against force for the trolley.

1.1   Give **one** conclusion that can be made from **Figure 2**.

....

[1]

1.2   Write down the formula that links force, mass and acceleration.

....

[1]

1.3   Calculate the mass of the system from **Figure 2**.

Mass = ... kg

[3]

[Total 5 marks]

2   A second student investigates how the mass of a trolley affects its motion down a fixed ramp. The accelerating force on the trolley is the component of the trolley's weight that acts along the ramp. The student adds masses to the trolley and each time measures its final speed at the bottom of the ramp to calculate its acceleration. Explain why this experiment will not correctly show the relationship between the mass and acceleration of the trolley.

....

....

....

....

....

[Total 2 marks]

Stopping Distances

1 Define the following terms: **Grade 4-6**

1.1 Thinking distance

....

[1]

1.2 Braking distance

....

[1]

[Total 2 marks]

2 The thinking distance for a driver in a car travelling at 40 mph is 12 m. The braking distance is 24 m. Calculate the car's stopping distance when it is travelling at 40 mph. **Grade 4-6**

Stopping Distance = ... m

[Total 1 mark]

3 When a vehicle's brakes are applied, energy is transferred away from the kinetic energy stores of the wheels. State what causes this and describe the effect it has on the brakes. **Grade 6-7**

....

....

....

....

[Total 2 marks]

4* Explain the importance of a car having brakes and tyres that are in good condition and the effect this will have on stopping distance and safety. **Grade 6-7**

....

....

....

....

....

....

....

....

....

[Total 6 marks]

Reaction Times

1 What is the typical reaction time for a person? *(Grade 4-6)*

☐ 1.3 – 1.8 s   ☐ 0.2 – 0.9 s   ☐ 0.01 – 0.02 s   ☐ 2.0 – 3.0 s

[Total 1 mark]

2 Give three things that could affect a person's reaction time. *(Grade 4-6)*

1. ....

2. ....

3. ....

[Total 3 marks]

3 A teacher tests the reaction times of two of her students by measuring how far a ruler falls vertically before the student catches it. *(Grade 4-6)*

3.1 Describe **one** other method that can be used to test people's reaction times.

....

[1]

3.2 **Table 1** shows the results. The values in the table show the distance the ruler falls in cm during each attempt. Complete the table by working out the average distance fallen by the ruler for each student.

Table 1

	Attempt 1	Attempt 2	Attempt 3	Average
Student A	7.0	7.1	6.9	....
Student B	8.4	8.2	8.3	....

[2]

3.3 Which student has the fastest average reaction time? Give a reason for your answer.

....

[1]

3.4 Suggest **two** ways the teacher could make the experiment a fair test.

....

....

[2]

3.5 The teacher then repeats the experiment. This time, she has a third student talk to the student being tested. Predict how this will affect the reaction times of both students A and B.

....

[1]

[Total 7 marks]

4 Describe the steps involved when using the ruler drop experiment to investigate reaction times.

Grade 6-7

....

....

....

....

....

....

[Total 5 marks]

5* A man is driving home late at night. He listens to loud music as he drives to keep himself alert. He is impatient to get home so drives quickly. Explain the safety implications of the man's actions.

Grade 6-7

....

....

....

....

....

....

....

[Total 4 marks]

6 A student tests his reaction time with a metre ruler using a ruler drop experiment. He catches the metre ruler after it has fallen 45.0 cm. Calculate his reaction time.

Grade 7-9

The acceleration due to gravity is 9.8 m/s^2.

Reaction time = ... s

[Total 4 marks]

Exam Practice Tip

For long explanation answers make sure you cover every point mentioned in the question. You won't get all of the marks if you miss out part of what they're asking for, no matter how much you write for the rest of your points.

Topic P5 — Forces

Momentum

The snippets below show the parts of a description of momentum.
Number each snippet 1 to 5 to show the correct order. The first one has been done for you.

| ☐ ...vector quantity and is equal to... | | **1** Momentum is a property of... |

| ☐ ...moving objects. | ☐ ...mass × velocity. | ☐ It is a... |

1 A motorbike is travelling at 25 m/s and has 5500 kg m/s of momentum. *Grade 4-6*

1.1 Write down the equation that links momentum, mass and velocity.

....

[1]

1.2 Calculate the mass of the motorbike.

Mass = ... kg

[3]

[Total 4 marks]

2 **Figure 1** and **Figure 2** show a Newton's cradle.
All of the balls on the cradle have the same mass. *Grade 6-7*

Figure 1   **Figure 2**

When a ball is lifted and allowed to hit the others as shown in **Figure 1**, it causes the last ball
in the line to move outwards, as shown in **Figure 2**. The balls in between appear to remain
stationary. The velocity of the first ball when it hits the second ball is equal to the velocity of
the final ball when it starts to move. Using conservation of momentum, explain this behaviour.

....

....

....

....

....

....

[Total 4 marks]

Transverse and Longitudinal Waves

1   A student produces two types of waves on a spring, A and B, as shown in **Figure 1**.

Figure 1

1.1 Draw a ring around the correct words to complete the sentence below.

Wave A is a [**transverse** / **longitudinal**] wave and wave B is a [**transverse** / **longitudinal**] wave.

[1]

1.2 Label the wavelength of wave A on **Figure 1**.

[1]

1.3 Define the term 'amplitude'.

....

[1]

1.4 Give **one** example of a transverse wave.

....

[1]

[Total 4 marks]

2   **Figure 2** shows a loudspeaker. It produces a sound wave with a frequency of 200 Hz. Sound waves are an example of a longitudinal wave.

Figure 2

2.1 Draw an arrow on **Figure 2** to show the direction in which the sound wave transfers energy.

[1]

2.2 Calculate the period of the sound wave.

Period = ... s

[2]

2.3 Describe the difference between a longitudinal wave and a transverse wave.

....

....

....

[2]

[Total 5 marks]

PRACTICAL

Experiments with Waves

1   **Figure 1** shows ripples on the surface of some water in a ripple tank. The signal generator producing the ripples is set to a frequency of 12 Hz. A student measures the distance between the first and last visible ripple as 18 cm, as shown in **Figure 1**.

Figure 1

18 cm

1.1 The student finds it difficult to measure the distance because the ripples are moving. Suggest and explain what the student could do to make the measurement easier.

....

....

....

[2]

1.2 Calculate the speed of the ripples in the water.

Speed = ... m/s

[3]

[Total 5 marks]

2*   Describe a method to measure the speed of waves on a string.   Grade 7-9

....

....

....

....

....

....

....

....

....

[Total 6 marks]

Topic P6 — Waves

Wave Behaviour and Electromagnetic Waves

Warm-Up

At the boundary with a new material, a wave can be reflected, absorbed or transmitted.
Draw a line to match each option to the correct definition.

wave is reflected   it passes through the material unaffected

wave is absorbed   it bounces back off the material

wave is transmitted   it transfers all energy to the material

---

1   Electromagnetic waves form a continuous spectrum. Grade 4-6

1.1   Use words from the box below to complete the following sentences.

a vacuum	glass	sound	longitudinal	transverse	water

All waves in the electromagnetic spectrum are ....

All electromagnetic waves travel at the same speed in ....

[2]

1.2   **Figure 1** shows a graph of intensity against wavelength for two objects at different temperatures.

Name the part of the electromagnetic spectrum that the peak wavelength of object B lies in.

....
[1]

Figure 1

Intensity (y-axis) vs Wavelength (x-axis). Object A curve (peak high), Object B curve (peak low, dashed). Infrared range marked near the start of the x-axis.

1.3   The peak wavelength for object A lies within the infrared range of the electromagnetic spectrum. Describe an example of infrared radiation transferring energy from a source to an absorber.

....

....
[2]

[Total 5 marks]

---

2   A man is wearing mirrored sunglasses. Anyone looking at him can see their reflection in the glasses but cannot see his eyes. The man can still see through the glasses. Grade 6-7

State what happens to the light as it passes from the surroundings to the mirrored sunglasses.

....

....
[Total 2 marks]

Topic P6 — Waves

Refraction

1   **Figure 1** shows wave fronts of light passing from air into glass. As the wave fronts enter the glass they slow down.

Figure 1

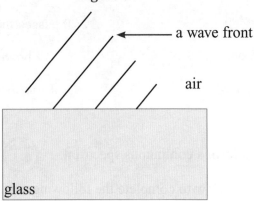

1.1   Complete the diagram in **Figure 1** by completing the wave fronts inside the glass.

[2]

1.2   Draw a ray on **Figure 1** to show how a light ray is refracted as it passes from air into glass. On your diagram, label the incident ray, refracted ray, and normal line.

[3]

[Total 5 marks]

2   A light ray crosses the boundary between two blocks, as shown in **Figure 2**.

Figure 2

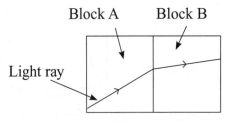

2.1   Explain how you can tell that blocks A and B in **Figure 2** are made from different materials.

....

[1]

2.2   Block B is a made from a type of glass. The light ray passes out of block B into a vacuum. Explain what happens to the direction and speed of the ray as it leaves block B.

....

....

....

[2]

[Total 3 marks]

Exam Practice Tip

Remember — each wave front represents the same point on a wave, so the distance between each is equal to a wavelength.

Topic P6 — Waves

Radio Waves

Tick the appropriate boxes to sort the radio-wave facts from the fiction.

	True	False
Long-wave radio can be transmitted across long distances.	☐	☐
Long-wave radio uses diffraction to follow the curve of the Earth's surface.	☐	☐
Short-wave radio can only be used over short distances.	☐	☐
Radio waves with very short wavelengths do not travel well through obstacles.	☐	☐

1* Describe how an electrical signal generates a radio wave in a TV signal transmitter. Explain how this radio wave can generate an electrical signal in a distant TV aerial.

Grade 6-7

....

....

....

....

....

....

....

[Total 4 marks]

2* A family from northern England are on holiday in France. They are unable to listen to their local FM radio station from back home. However, they are still able to listen to the same long-wave radio broadcasts as they do at home. Explain why.

Grade 7-9

....

....

....

....

....

....

....

....

....

....

....

[Total 6 marks]

 ☐   ☐   ☐

EM Waves and Their Uses

1   A student uses a microwave oven to cook a jacket potato.   (Grade 6-7)

1.1   Describe how microwaves cook the potato in the microwave oven.

....

....

....

           [3]

1.2   The potato is placed in the microwave oven on a glass plate.
      Explain why the glass plate does not get hot when the microwave oven is used.

....

....

....

           [2]

1.3   State the other type of electromagnetic radiation which is commonly used to cook food.

....

           [1]

1.4   Microwaves can also be used to communicate with satellites. Explain why the microwaves used
      for communications must have different wavelengths to those used in microwave ovens.

....

....

....

....

           [4]

           [Total 10 marks]

2   A police helicopter has an infrared camera attached to its base. The camera
can be used to detect people trying to hide in the dark. Explain the advantages   (Grade 7-9)
of using an infrared camera rather than a normal camera for this purpose.

....

....

....

....

           [Total 3 marks]

More Uses of EM Waves

Warm-Up

Sort the EM uses below into the table. Some of the uses may appear in more than one column.

Uses of EM waves

A artificial suntanning

B fibre optic data transmission

C energy efficient light bulbs

D revealing invisible ink

E medical imaging of bones

F cancer treatment

UV Rays	Visible Light	X-rays	Gamma Rays

1 X-rays and gamma rays can both be used in medical imaging. Grade 6-7

1.1 Briefly describe how a medical tracer can be used to create an internal body image.

....

....

....

[2]

1.2 Explain why gamma rays are suitable for medical imaging.

....

....

[1]

1.3 Explain how X-rays are used to form images of a patient's skeleton.

....

....

....

....

[3]

1.4 Exposure to both X-rays and gamma rays can be dangerous to humans. Suggest **one** precaution taken by medical workers who use X-rays or gamma rays when imaging patients.

....

[1]

[Total 7 marks]

Exam Practice Tip

You may be asked to explain why a given electromagnetic wave is suited to a particular use. So make sure you understand the properties of the different electromagnetic wave types, and know some of their most common uses.

PRACTICAL Investigating Infrared Radiation

Figure 1

1 A student uses a Leslie cube, shown in **Figure 1**, to investigate how different materials radiate energy.
A Leslie cube is a hollow cube whose faces are made out of different materials.

Grade
6-7

The student fills the cube with hot water and places his hand near to each surface.
He records how warm his hand feels in front of each surface.
The four sides of the cube are matte black, shiny black, matte white and shiny white.

1.1 Predict which side the student's hand would feel warmest in front of.

....
[1]

1.2 Predict which side the student's hand would feel coolest in front of.

....
[1]

1.3 Suggest **one** way to improve the student's experiment.

....
[1]
[Total 3 marks]

2* A student wants to investigate how effective different surfaces are at absorbing radiation. Describe a method the student could use to do this.
Your answer should include ways the student can make his investigation a fair test.

Grade
7-9

....

....

....

....

....

....

....

....

....

....

....

[Total 6 marks]

Topic P6 — Waves

Dangers of Electromagnetic Waves

1 Some types of electromagnetic wave can be harmful to people. **Grade 6-7**

1.1 Describe how X-rays and gamma rays can cause cancer.

....

....

[2]

1.2 Another type of harmful electromagnetic radiation is ultraviolet radiation.
Give two damaging effects of ultraviolet light.

....

....

[2]

[Total 4 marks]

2 **Table 1** lists the radiation doses for some common medical procedures. **Grade 7-9**

Table 1

Procedure	Typical effective dose (mSv)	Lifetime additional risk of fatal cancer per examination
X-ray image of skull	0.07	1 in 300 000
X-ray image of lower spine	1.3	1 in 15 000
CT scan of head	2	1 in 10 000

2.1 The lifetime additional risk of fatal cancer from a CT scan of the chest is 1 in 2500.
Use **Table 1** to estimate the typical effective dose of a CT scan of the chest.

Typical effective dose = ... mSv

[2]

2.2* Nuclear medicine scans use gamma rays to create images of internal organs, but have a high
effective radiation dosage. Discuss the risks involved in performing this type of scan, and why
the procedure might go ahead despite the risks.

....

....

....

....

....

....

....

....

[6]

[Total 8 marks]

Permanent and Induced Magnets

Complete the sentence using one of the words below.

non-contact   contact   nuclear

Magnetic force is an example of a .... force.

1   Magnets have magnetic fields.   (Grade 4-6)

1.1 Define the term magnetic field.

   ....

   ....

   [1]

1.2 Name **two** magnetic materials.

   1. ....

   2. ....

   [2]

1.3 **Figure 1** shows a bar magnet. Draw the magnetic field lines onto the diagram in **Figure 1**.

Figure 1

| N   S |

[2]

1.4 Which of the following statements are correct for magnets? Tick **two** boxes.

Like poles attract each other.   ☐

The magnetic field at the north pole of a magnet is always stronger than at the south pole.   ☐

The closer together the magnetic field lines, the stronger the magnetic field.   ☐

Magnetic field lines point from the north pole to the south pole of a magnet.   ☐

The force between a magnet and a magnetic material can be attractive or repulsive.   ☐

[2]

[Total 7 marks]

2 A block of cobalt is held in place near to a bar magnet, as shown in **Figure 2**.

Figure 2

N	S

bar magnet   cobalt • P

2.1 A steel paperclip is placed against the block of cobalt at point P, shown on **Figure 2**.
The paperclip sticks to the block of cobalt. State why this is the case.

....

....

....

[2]

2.2 The bar magnet is removed. Explain what happens to the paperclip.

....

....

[2]

[Total 4 marks]

3 A student wants to investigate the magnetic field of a horseshoe magnet, shown in **Figure 3**.

Figure 3

3.1* Explain how a compass could be used to determine the magnetic field of the magnet.

....

....

....

....

....

....

[4]

3.2 State what would happen to the compass if you were to move it far away from any magnets.
Explain why this would happen.

....

....

[2]

[Total 6 marks]

Topic P7 — Magnetism and Electromagnetism

Electromagnetism

1 **Figure 1** shows a wire which has a current flowing through it. The arrow shows the direction of the current.

Figure 1

1.1 The flow of charge creates a magnetic field around the wire.
On **Figure 1**, draw field lines showing the direction of the magnetic field created.

[2]

1.2 The direction of the current is reversed. State the effect this will have on the magnetic field.

....

[1]

1.3 State **one** way in which the magnetic field strength around the wire could be increased.

....

[1]

[Total 4 marks]

2 A current-carrying solenoid has a magnetic field outside it similar to a bar magnet. (Grade 7-9)

2.1 State **one** way in which the magnetic field strength of a solenoid can be increased.

....

[1]

2.2 The north pole of a magnet is brought near to the current-carrying solenoid as shown in **Figure 2**. State whether the north pole is **attracted** or **repelled** by the solenoid. Explain why.

Figure 2

N

....

....

....

[3]

[Total 4 marks]

Exam Practice Tip

A current carrying-wire will always produce a magnetic field around it. No matter what position the wire is in, or what shape it's been bent into, the magnetic field around it will always depend on the direction of the current.

The Motor Effect

1 A 0.75 m section of wire, carrying a current of 0.4 A, is placed into a magnetic field. When the wire is perpendicular to the field, it experiences a force of 1.2 N. Calculate the magnetic flux density of the field, using an equation from the Equations List. Give the correct unit in your answer.

Magnetic flux density = ...

Unit = ...

[Total 3 marks]

2 A student carries out an experiment using a horseshoe magnet and an iron bar connected in a circuit. Part of the set-up is shown in **Figure 2**.

Figure 2

Birds-eye view of experiment set-up.

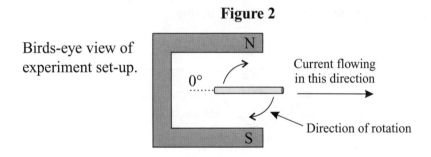

The student rotates the iron bar 90° clockwise and measures the force acting on the bar as she does so. She then plots her results on a graph of force, *F*, against angle of rotation, *θ*.

Which of the following graphs shows a sketch of her results? Tick **one** box.

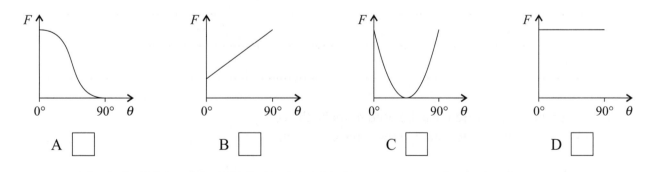

[Total 1 mark]

Exam Practice Tip

The size of the force acting on a current-carrying wire in a magnetic field depends on four variables — the magnetic field strength, the size of the current through the wire, the length of the wire in the field and the angle of the wire to the field.

Topic P7 — Magnetism and Electromagnetism

Electric Motors

1 A wire is placed between two magnets, as shown in **Figure 1**. A current is flowing through the wire, in the direction shown.

Figure 1

N   S   ↑current   N   S

What will happen to the wire? Tick **one** box.

It will move to the left. ☐

It will move away from you, into the paper. ☐

It will move towards you, out of the paper. ☐

It will remain stationary. ☐

[Total 1 mark]

2 **Figure 2** shows part of a basic dc motor. A coil of wire is positioned between two magnetic poles and allowed to rotate.

Figure 2

N   S   − +

2.1 State the direction in which the coil will turn (**anticlockwise** or **clockwise**).

....

[1]

2.2 Explain why the coil turns.

....

....

....

[2]

2.3 Explain how a dc current can be used to make the coil in **Figure 2** continue to rotate in the same direction.

....

....

....

....

[2]

[Total 5 marks]

Biology Mixed Questions

1 Alcohol is metabolised in the liver using alcohol dehydrogenase enzymes. *(Grade 4-6)*

1.1 State **one** function of the liver, other than alcohol metabolism.

....

[1]

1.2 Which of the following sentences about enzymes is **true**? Tick **one** box.

☐ Enzymes speed up chemical reactions in living organisms.

☐ Enzymes are used up in chemical reactions.

☐ Enzymes are products of digestion.

☐ Enzymes are the building blocks of all living organisms.

[1]

A scientist was investigating the effect of pH on the rate of activity of alcohol dehydrogenase. **Figure 1** shows a graph of his results.

Figure 1

1.3 What is the optimum pH for the enzyme?

....

[1]

1.4 Suggest and explain the effect an acid with a pH of 1 would have on the enzyme.

....

....

....

[3]

1.5 Which of the following statements about alcohol is **not true**? Tick **one** box.

☐ Too much alcohol can cause liver disease.

☐ Alcohol is a risk factor for lung cancer.

☐ Alcohol can cause brain damage.

☐ Alcohol can affect unborn babies.

[1]

[Total 7 marks]

2 A group of students were investigating the effect of air flow on the rate of transpiration. They set up their apparatus as shown in **Figure 2**.

Figure 2

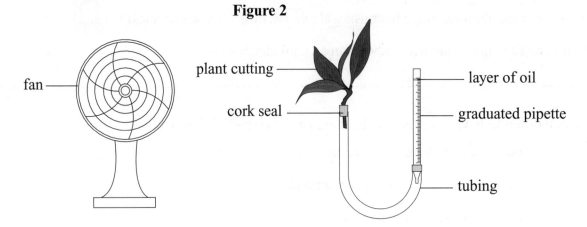

fan

plant cutting

cork seal

layer of oil

graduated pipette

tubing

2.1 The tubing and graduated pipette were filled with water.
Suggest why a layer of oil was added to the surface of the water in the pipette.

....

[1]

The students recorded the change in the volume of water in the pipette over 30 minutes, in normal conditions. They repeated this five times. They then carried out these steps with the fan turned on to simulate windy conditions. **Table 1** shows their results.

Table 1

	Repeat	1	2	3	4	5	Mean
Water uptake in 30 minutes (cm³)	Still Air	1.2	1.2	1.0	0.8	1.1	1.1
	Moving Air	2.0	1.8	2.3	1.9	1.7	1.9

2.2 Draw a bar chart to show the mean water uptake for still air and moving air.

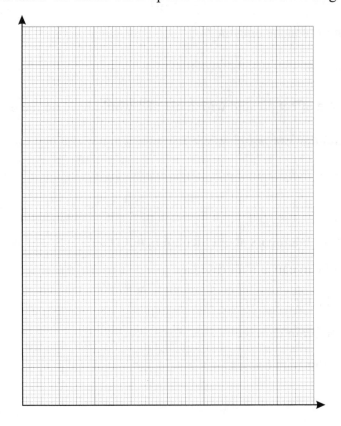

[2]

2.3 Describe the relationship between air flow around the plant and transpiration rate.

....

[1]

2.4 Explain the effect of air flow on the rate of transpiration.

....

....

....

[2]

2.5 Calculate the range of the results for still air.

Range = ... cm³

[1]

2.6 The rate of transpiration can be calculated using the formula:

$$\text{rate of transpiration} = \frac{\text{mean volume of water uptake}}{\text{time taken}}$$

Calculate the rate of transpiration for the plant in moving air.
Give your answer in cm³/hour.

.... cm³/hour

[2]

[Total 9 marks]

3 Aerobic respiration transfers energy from glucose. Grade 6-7

3.1 Name the subcellular structures where aerobic respiration takes place.

....

[1]

3.2 Complete the word equation for aerobic respiration.

.... + ... → .... + ...

[2]

3.3 Outline the role that glucose plays in the production of proteins in the body.

....

....

....

....

[3]

[Total 6 marks]

Biology Mixed Questions

4   The endocrine system uses hormones to produce effects within the body.   (Grade 6-7)

4.1 Outline how a hormone travels from a gland to its target organ in the body.

....

....

[2]

The menstrual cycle is controlled by hormones.

Figure 3 shows the change in the levels of these hormones during one menstrual cycle. It also shows the change in the lining of the uterus.

Figure 3

4.2 Which line in **Figure 3** represents oestrogen? Tick **one** box.

☐ A   ☐ B   ☐ C   ☐ D

[1]

4.3 Which line in **Figure 3** represents luteinising hormone? Tick **one** box.

☐ A   ☐ B   ☐ C   ☐ D

[1]

4.4 What is the function of luteinising hormone?

....

[1]

4.5 Where in the body is progesterone produced?

....

[1]

4.6 Taking the combined pill keeps the level of oestrogen in the body constantly high. Explain how this reduces fertility.

....

....

[2]

[Total 8 marks]

5 A student was investigating the effect of limiting factors on the rate of photosynthesis by green algae.

 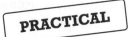

The student set up two boiling tubes as shown in **Figure 4**. She also set up a third tube that did not contain any algae. The colour of the indicator solution changes as follows:

Figure 4

- At atmospheric CO_2 concentration, the indicator is red.
- At low CO_2 concentrations, the indicator is purple.
- At high CO_2 concentrations, the indicator is yellow.

The student covered one of the boiling tubes containing algae with foil. All three tubes were left for several hours at room temperature with a constant light source. The colour of the indicator solution was then recorded. The results are shown in **Table 2**.

Table 2

	Algae?	Foil?	Indicator colour at start	Indicator colour at end
Tube 1	yes	yes	red	yellow
Tube 2	yes	no	red	purple
Tube 3	no	no	red	red

5.1 Name the waste product of photosynthesis.

....

[1]

5.2 Name the limiting factor of photosynthesis that is being investigated in this experiment.

....

[1]

5.3 At the end of the experiment, which tube has the highest carbon dioxide concentration? Tick **one** box.

☐ Tube 1 ☐ Tube 2 ☐ Tube 3

[1]

5.4 Explain the results of Tube 1 and Tube 2.

....

....

....

....

....

[4]

5.5 Give **two** variables that needed to be controlled in this experiment.

....

....

[2]

A scientist investigating the effect of limiting factors on photosynthesis sketched the graph shown in **Figure 5**.

Figure 5

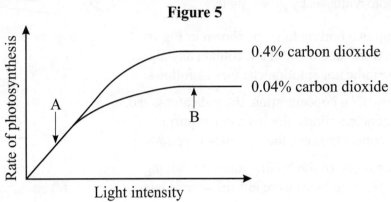

5.6 What is the limiting factor at point **A**? Explain your answer.

....

....

[2]

5.7 Name the limiting factor at point **B**.

....

[1]

[Total 12 marks]

6   In pea plants, seed shape is controlled by a single gene.   Grade 7-9

The allele for round seed shape is R and the allele for wrinkled seed shape is r.
R is a dominant allele and r is recessive.

6.1 What is the genotype of a pea plant that is homozygous dominant for seed shape?

....

[1]

6.2 What is the phenotype of a pea plant that is heterozygous for seed shape?

....

[1]

6.3 Two pea plants were crossed. All of the offspring produced had the genotype **Rr**.
Construct a Punnett square to find the genotypes of the parent plants.

Genotypes: .... and ....

[3]

[Total 5 marks]

Chemistry Mixed Questions

1 A substance can be classified as an element, a compound or a mixture. *(Grade 4-6)*

1.1 Draw a line to connect each type of substance with an example of it.

compound		bromine water
element		helium
mixture		iron oxide

[2]

1.2 Formulations are a special type of mixture. Explain what is meant by the term 'formulation'.

....

....

[2]

[Total 4 marks]

2 Salt is the common name for sodium chloride. Salt can be obtained by mining rock salt, which also contains sand and insoluble bits of rock. *(Grade 4-6)*

2.1 How could the sand and bits of rock be separated from the salt? Tick **one** box.

Dissolve the rock salt in water and distill the water. ☐

Dissolve the rock salt in water and crystallise the sodium chloride. ☐

Dissolve the rock salt in water and filter. ☐

Dissolve the rock salt in water and carry out chromatography. ☐

[1]

2.2 Explain why sodium chloride is classified as a compound.

....

....

[2]

2.3 The structure of sodium chloride is shown in **Figure 1**.

Figure 1

● $= Cl^-$

○ $= Na^+$

State the type of bonding in sodium chloride.

....

[1]

[Total 4 marks]

3 Oxygen atoms have the electronic structure 2,6. (Grade 4-6)

3.1 State which group of the periodic table oxygen is in.
Explain your answer with reference to the electronic structure of oxygen.

Group: ....

Explanation: ....

[2]

3.2 Oxygen can react to form oxide ions. Predict, with reasoning the charge on an oxide ion.

....

....

[2]

3.3 When magnesium reacts with oxygen, it forms magnesium oxide. What type of reaction does magnesium undergo? Tick **one** box.

Displacement ☐   Oxidation ☐

Electrolysis ☐   Reduction ☐

[1]

[Total 5 marks]

4 Chlorine is a Group 7 element that exists as molecules of Cl_2. (Grade 4-6)

4.1 Complete the dot-and-cross diagram below to show the bonding in Cl_2.
You only need to show the outer electron shells.

Cl   Cl

[2]

4.2 Chlorine has two main isotopes — ^{35}Cl and ^{37}Cl. Explain the term 'isotope'.

....

....

[2]

4.3 Describe a test you could carry out for chlorine. **PRACTICAL**
Include any observations you would expect.

....

....

[2]

4.4 Predict what happens if you mix chlorine water and sodium iodide solution. Explain your answer.

....

....

[2]

[Total 8 marks]

5 When sodium hydrogencarbonate reacts with ethanoic acid, the temperature of the surroundings decreases. (Grade 4-6)

5.1 Is this reaction endothermic or exothermic?

....

[1]

5.2 Will the energy of the products be higher or lower than the energy of the reactants?

....

[1]

5.3 Explain the temperature change of this reaction in terms of the energy required to break the bonds in the reactants and the energy released when bonds are formed in the products.

....

....

[2]

5.4 Suggest one practical use of this reaction.

....

[1]

[Total 5 marks]

6 Pentane, C_5H_{12}, and decane, $C_{10}H_{22}$, are both hydrocarbons in the same homologous series. (Grade 6-7)

6.1 What homologous series do pentane and decane belong to?

....

[1]

6.2 Name a process that could be used to separate pentane from decane.

....

[1]

6.3 Name a process that could be used to produce pentane from decane.

....

[1]

6.4 Predict, with reasoning, whether pentane or decane will have a higher boiling point.

....

....

....

[3]

6.5 Write a balanced symbol equation for the complete combustion of pentane in oxygen to form carbon dioxide and water.

....

[2]

[Total 8 marks]

7 Iron and silver are both metals. Iron has a melting point of 1538 °C, whilst silver has a melting point of 962 °C. Iron boils at 2862 °C and silver boils at 2162 °C. *(Grade 6-7)*

7.1 Describe the bonding in metals, like iron and silver, when they are solid.

....

....

....

[3]

7.2 What states would iron and silver be in if they were both at a temperature of 1000 °C?

Iron: .... Silver: ....

[2]

7.3 Use the information above to predict which metal has the strongest bonds. Explain your answer.

....

....

[3]

[Total 8 marks]

8 Copper is a metal found in a number of everyday mixtures and compounds. *(Grade 6-7)*

8.1 State, with reasoning, how you would extract copper from copper oxide.

....

....

[2]

8.2 Describe how bioleaching can be used to extract copper from low grade ores.

....

....

....

[3]

8.3 Copper can be drawn out into thin wires which are used in electrical cables.
Explain **two** ways in which the bonding and structure of copper make it suitable for this.

....

....

[2]

8.4 Statues can be made from bronze, an alloy of copper that contains tin. Explain how the structure of bronze makes it more suitable than pure copper for this use.

....

....

....

[3]

[Total 10 marks]

9 Models of the structure of the atom went through a lot of development in the early 1900s. [Grade 6-7]

9.1 Ernest Rutherford set up an experiment which involved firing alpha particles at a piece of gold foil. The results of the experiment did not match the prediction of what should have happened if the plum pudding model had been correct. Describe the model that Rutherford developed to replace the plum pudding model.

....

....

[2]

9.2 Describe the model of the atom used today, with reference to protons, neutrons and electrons.

....

....

....

[3]

[Total 5 marks]

PRACTICAL

10 When the following reaction is carried out in an unsealed reaction flask, the mass changes over the course of the reaction: $2HCl_{(aq)} + Na_2CO_{3(aq)} \rightarrow 2NaCl_{(aq)} + H_2O_{(l)} + CO_{2(g)}$ [Grade 6-7]

10.1 Explain, in terms of the particle model, why the mass of the reaction flask changes in the reaction.

....

....

....

[3]

10.2 The volume of gas produced by the reaction mixture can be used to investigate how the concentration of acid affects the rate of the reaction. Write a method the student could use to carry out this experiment.

....

....

....

....

....

....

[6]

10.3 At the start of an experiment, the gas syringe was empty. After 30 s, it contained 12.0 cm³ of gas. Calculate the mean rate of reaction during this time.

Mean rate = ... cm³/s

[2]

[Total 11 marks]

Chemistry Mixed Questions

11 Carbon dioxide is a greenhouse gas found naturally in Earth's atmosphere. (Grade 6-7)

11.1 Millions of years ago, the amount of carbon dioxide in the atmosphere was much higher than it is today. State **two** ways in which carbon dioxide was removed from the atmosphere.

....

....

[2]

11.2 Human activities are increasing the amount of carbon dioxide in the atmosphere. Name **one** other greenhouse gas that is increasing due to human activity. Give an activity causing this increase.

....

....

[2]

11.3*Give examples of pollutant gases, other than carbon dioxide and the one mentioned in your answer to 11.2, that are produced by human activity. Explain how these gases form and how they impact on the environment and human health.

....

....

....

....

....

....

[6]

[Total 10 marks]

12 A student reacts lithium in an excess of water to produce lithium hydroxide and hydrogen gas. The equation for this reaction is: $2Li + 2H_2O \rightarrow 2LiOH + H_2$ (Grade 6-7)
Atomic masses, A_r: Li = 7, O = 16, H = 1

12.1 Calculate the relative formula mass of lithium hydroxide.

Relative formula mass = ...
[1]

12.2 A student performed this reaction using 1.75 g of lithium. How many moles is this?

Number of moles = ... mol
[2]

12.3 Use the symbol equation to calculate the mass, in g, of lithium hydroxide that would be produced using 0.50 mol lithium and an excess of water.

Mass = ... g
[3]

[Total 6 marks]

Chemistry Mixed Questions

13 When zinc sulfate solution is electrolysed, the reaction at the cathode is: $2H^+_{(aq)} + 2e^- \rightarrow H_{2(g)}$ (Grade 7-9)

13.1 Explain why it is easier to discharge hydrogen rather than zinc, and what this tells you about the relative abilities of hydrogen and zinc to form positive ions.

....

....

[2]

13.2 What type of reaction takes place at the cathode? Explain your answer.

....

....

[2]

13.3 Write a balanced half equation for the reaction that occurs at the anode.

....

[2]

[Total 6 marks]

14 Some of the properties and reactions of different Group 1 metals are shown in **Table 1**. (Grade 7-9)

Table 1

Metal	Melting point (°C)	Typical ion that forms in reactions	Reaction with acid
Lithium	181	+1	vigorous
Sodium		+1	very vigorous, ignites
Potassium	63	+1	extremely vigorous, ignites

14.1*Describe the similarities and differences in how lithium and sodium react, as shown in **Table 1**. Give reasons for them, based on the electronic structures of the atoms.

....

....

....

....

....

....

[6]

14.2 Using the data in the table, predict the melting point of sodium.

melting point = ... °C

[1]

[Total 7 marks]

Physics Mixed Questions

1   A student uses a compass to investigate magnetic field patterns.   (Grade 4-6)

   1.1   The compass contains a permanent bar magnet.
Describe the difference between a permanent magnet and an induced magnet.

....

....

                                                                                    [2]

   1.2   The student moves the compass around the current-carrying solenoid shown in **Figure 1**.
The student uses the compass to plot the magnetic field produced by the solenoid.
Sketch the magnetic field produced by the solenoid on **Figure 1**.

Figure 1

direction of current

                                                                                [3]

                                                                 [Total 5 marks]

2   When a nucleus decays, it can emit alpha, beta or gamma radiation.   (Grade 4-6)

   2.1   Use words from the box below to complete the passage about radioactive decay.
You can only use a word once and you do not need to use all of the words.

can	stable	cannot	unstable	forced	random

Radioactive decay is where a nucleus releases radiation to become more ....

It is a .... process, which means you .... predict

which individual nucleus in a sample will decay next.

                                                                                [2]

   2.2   The term 'activity' can be used when describing a radioactive source.
Define activity and state the unit it is measured in.

....

                                                                                [2]

   2.3   The term 'half-life' can also be used when describing a source of radiation.
Define half-life in terms of activity.

....

                                                                                [1]

                                                                 [Total 5 marks]

3   **Figure 2** shows an electric fan.

Figure 2

3.1   The fan is connected to the mains with a cable that contains three wires.
What is the name of this type of cable? Tick **one** box.

☐ three-colour cable   ☐ two-core cable   ☐ three-core cable   ☐ triple cable

[1]

3.2   Complete **Table 1** to show the properties of each wire in the cable.

Table 1

Name of wire	Colour of insulation	Potential difference (V)
Live	....	....
....	blue	....
....	....	0

[3]

3.3   The fan works by transferring energy. Use phrases from the box below to complete the passage.
You can only use a phrase once and you do not need to use all of the phrases.

electrically   thermal   by heating   kinetic   mechanically   elastic potential

Energy is transferred .... from the mains supply to the

.... energy store of the fan's blades.

[2]

3.4   The fan has a power of 30 W. Calculate the energy transferred by the fan in 30 minutes.

Energy transferred = ... J

[2]

[Total 8 marks]

4   A student tests the relationship between potential difference and current for a filament bulb.

4.1 **Figure 3** shows four *I-V* characteristics.
Tick the box under the *I-V* characteristic for a filament bulb.

Figure 3

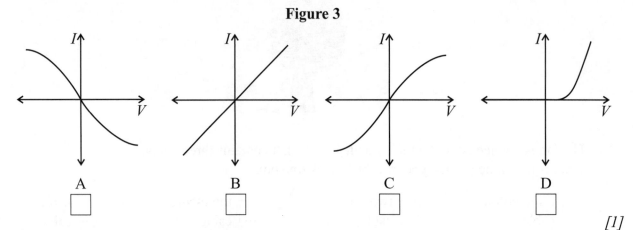

[1]

At a potential difference of 240 V the current through the bulb is 1.2 A.

4.2 Write down the equation that links potential difference, current and resistance.

....

[1]

4.3 Calculate the resistance of the bulb.

Resistance = ... Ω
[2]

[Total 4 marks]

5   Waves on a string are an example of a transverse wave.

5.1 Which of the following are examples of transverse waves? Tick **two** boxes.

 sound waves   water ripples   ultrasound waves   gamma rays

[1]

A wave on a string has a wavelength of 60 cm and a frequency of 40 Hz.

5.2 Calculate the period of the wave. Give your answer in milliseconds.

Period = ... ms
[3]

5.3 Write down the equation that links wave speed, frequency and wavelength.

....

[1]

5.4 Calculate the speed of the wave.

Speed = ... m/s
[2]

[Total 7 marks]

6 A child is playing with a remote-controlled toy car.

Figure 4

6.1 **Figure 4** shows an incomplete force diagram for the toy. Complete the force diagram to show the resultant resistive force acting on the car as it travels at a steady speed.

[2]

6.2 Write down the equation that links distance travelled, speed and time.

....

[1]

6.3 Calculate the distance the car travels in 30 seconds at a steady speed of 5.0 m/s.

Distance travelled = ... m

[2]

6.4 The car has a mass of 0.50 kg.
Calculate the energy in the kinetic energy store of the car as it travels at 5.0 m/s.

Energy = ... J

[2]

The car is powered by an electric motor. The efficiency of the motor is 65%.
During a short journey, 1200 J of energy was transferred to the motor.

6.5 Write down the equation that links efficiency, the useful output energy transfer and the useful input energy transfer.

....

[1]

6.6 Calculate the useful output energy transferred by the motor during the journey.

Output energy = ... J

[2]

[Total 11 marks]

Physics Mixed Questions

7   A man goes for a bike ride. **Figure 5** shows a velocity-time graph for the man's journey.

Figure 5

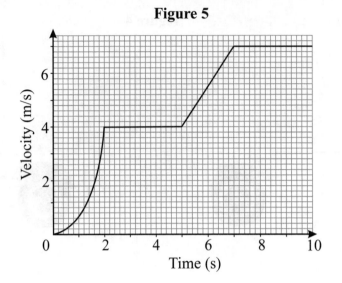

7.1   Describe the motion of the man:

During the first two seconds of the journey: ....

At four seconds from the start of the journey: ....

Between 5-7 s from the start of the journey: ....

[3]

7.2   Calculate the acceleration of the cyclist 6 seconds from the start of his bike ride.

Acceleration = ... m/s²

[3]

7.3   Ten seconds after the beginning of the cyclist's bike ride, a car turns out of a junction 12 m
in front of him. The cyclist is alert and quickly applies the bike's brakes, which provide a constant
braking force of 440 N. The combined mass of the man and the bicycle is 83 kg.
Calculate the deceleration of the bicycle.

Deceleration = ... m/s²

[3]

7.4   Use your answer from 7.3 to determine whether or not the cyclist will hit the car.
Write down any assumptions you make about the cyclist's reaction time.

....

[5]

[Total 14 marks]

8   A student is investigating the properties of visible light. She uses the set-up in **Figure 6** to test how different materials refract light.

She begins by shining a thin ray of white light into one block of material and marking where the light ray emerges from the block. She then places a block of a different material next to the first block, leaving no air gap. She repeats this for a range of transparent and translucent materials.

Figure 6

8.1 Complete the wave front diagram in **Figure 8** for the light ray crossing the boundary between diamond and air.

[2]

8.2* Explain why the light ray refracts when it crosses the boundary between diamond and air. Your answer should refer to the wave fronts drawn in **Figure 8**.

....

....

....

....

....

....

....

....

....

....

[6]

[Total 8 marks]

9 A student is designing a basic electronic toy. He wants the toy to be able to light up and spin around. He creates a basic circuit of a battery connected to a motor. He connects two filament bulbs and a fixed resistor in parallel to the motor. The two bulbs and the resistor are all in series with each other. The bulbs and the motor can be switched on and off separately.

9.1 Draw the circuit diagram for the circuit created by the student.

[5]

9.2 The student turns on the motor alone. The potential difference across the motor is 6.0 V and a current of 70.0 mA flows through the motor. After 15 minutes, the student switches off the motor and measures the temperature of the motor's casing.
He finds that it has increased by 7.0 °C.

The motor's casing has a mass of 25.0 g.
The material it is made from has a specific heat capacity of 120 J/kg °C.
Calculate the amount of energy that is usefully transferred by the motor in 15 minutes.
You can assume that all energy not transferred to thermal energy store of the motor's casing is usefully transferred.

Energy usefully transferred = ... J
[5]

9.3 Explain **one** modification that the student could make to the toy to make it more efficient.

....

....

....
[2]
[Total 12 marks]

SAHQ41